Vegan Keto

Your Essential 100% Plant-Based Whole Foods Ketogenic Diet. Super Tasty and Healthy Low-Carb Recipes Cookbook to Weight Loss Naturally and Reset Your Body. Meal Prep included.

Dr AMY VOGEL FUNG

Licence to use the book

You must not in any circumstances:

(a)   publish, republish, sell, license, sub-license, rent, transfer, broadcast, distribute or redistribute the book or any part of the book;

(b)   edit, modify, adapt or alter the book or any part of the book;

(c)   use the book or any part of the book in any way that is unlawful or in breach of any person's legal rights under any applicable law, or in any way that is offensive, indecent, discriminatory or otherwise objectionable;

(d)   use the book or any part of the book to compete with us, whether directly or indirectly]

(e)   use the book or any part of the book for a commercial purpose.

You must retain, and must not delete, obscure or remove, all copyright notices and other proprietary notices in the book. The rights granted to you by this disclaimer are personal to you, and you must not permit any third party to exercise these rights. If you breach this disclaimer, then the licence set out above will be automatically terminated upon such breach (whether or not we notify you of termination).

Upon the termination of the licence, you will promptly and irrevocably delete from your computer systems and other electronic devices any copies of the book in your possession or control and will permanently destroy any paper or other copies of the book in your possession or control.

Disclaimer

The information provided in this book is designed to provide helpful information on the subjects discussed and content herein are provided for educational and entertainment purposes only.

The content and information contained in this book have been compiled from sources deemed reliable, and it is accurate to the best of the Author's knowledge, information, and belief.

Although the author and publisher have made every effort to ensure that the information in this book was correct at press time, without any errors and/or omissions, the author and publisher do not assume and hereby disclaim any liability to any party for any loss, damage, or disruption caused by errors or omissions, whether such errors or omission results from negligence, accident, or any other cause.

Further, changes are periodically made to this book as and when needed. Any liability, in terms of inattention or otherwise, by any usage or abuse of any policies, processes, or directions contained within is the solitary and utter responsibility of the recipient reader.

Under no circumstances will any legal responsibility or blame be held against the publisher for any reparation, damages, or monetary loss due to the information herein, either directly or indirectly. You agree that by continuing to read this book, where appropriate and/or necessary, you shall consult a professional (including but not limited to your doctor, attorney, or financial advisor or such other advisor as needed) before using any of the suggested remedies, techniques, or information in this book.

The information contained in this book and its contents is not meant to be used, nor should it be used, to diagnose or treat any medical condition and is not designed to replace or take the place of any form of medical, financial, legal or other professional advice or services, as may be required. Nothing in shared in this book is intended to be any kind of advice. The reader is responsible for his or her own actions and agrees to accept all risks of using the information presented inside this book.

Table of Content

Introduction

I am thrilled you have decided to include the Vegan Keto Plan as part of your new way of eating. I have filled it with tons of recipes to meet your desires for breakfast, lunch, dinner, and desserts. Everyone will surely find a new favorite!

Many say you are vegan because of the animals. If you have ever had an emotional attachment with an animal, many believe this is the sentiment that can lead to using veganism. The vegan way of eating was described early in 1944 by the Vegan Society. As time passed, the vegan society was defined as a philosophy and approach of living.

Combine the ketogenic techniques to your dieting plan and enjoy delicious meals without the added stress of knowing whether you are carb-friendly. You will find a ton of new recipes using the keto diet plan. Many are listed as vegan-friendly, whereas many others are also vegan-adaptable. The choice is yours whether you go total vegan or stay within the ketogenic guidelines, as explained throughout your new cookbook.

Let's Begin!

Chapter 1: The Ketogenic Diet Explained

You have to realize the adoption time of the ketogenic diet plan can take anywhere from two to four weeks or more. For some, it can take as much as six to eight weeks. It takes time because your body cannot instantly switch over to using fat as a fuel source. You may be experiencing low energy, withdrawal-type symptoms, fatigue, or headaches, but they will pass as your body adjusts.

Make use of your food processor, Instant Pot, slow cooker or crockpot, or an immersion blender to prepare delicious meals using your ketogenic meal plan. Some recipes might not be 100 % keto-friendly. Adjust the ingredients to your own discretion. Remember this Formula: Total Carbs minus (-) Fiber = Net Carbs. This is the logic used for each of the recipes included in this cookbook and guidelines.

You will need to formulate a game plan as you begin your ketogenic diet plan. That will include keeping track of your macronutrients. You can use any form you choose, whether it is saving a written journal or using an app. Use these for assistance:

Standard Keto Calculator: You will achieve the perfect mixture of the traditional keto diet plan of 5% carbs, 25% protein, and 70% ratios. (This is a general ratio.) Begin your weight loss process by making a habit of checking your levels when you want to know what essentials your body needs during your dieting plan. You will document your personal information, such as height and weight. The Internet calculator will provide you with essential math.

Check Units of Measurement: Many of the recipes you will discover over the Internet, or other sources will be listed using the Imperial or Metric system. Use this link as a quick and easy conversion chart.

Types Of Keto Plans Used

Standard Ketogenic Diet (SKD): As the name suggests, this variation of the ketogenic diet can be considered a baseline plan. It requires adherents to continuously consume high amounts of fat, low amounts of carbs, and moderate amounts of protein every day. In addition to managing weight loss, this variation of the diet is excellent for kick-starting weight loss.

In early phases of the keto diet, it's common to experience lower than average levels of energy – as the body is still transitioning to a state where it can efficiently process fats for fuel. This variation of the diet is not recommended in the long-term for those who plan on extensive exercising, as it probably won't provide the required amount of protein needed to promote healthy muscle growth.

SKD is a great place to start for those who follow a more sedentary lifestyle, those who are dealing with extreme weight issues, and those who have had a difficult time losing weight using other means. Ultimately this variation of the diet will control the urge for additional carbohydrates, regulate hunger, and promote weight loss with or without exercise.

Targeted Ketogenic Diet (TKD): This form of the plan allows carb intake between 25 and 50 grams of carbs whenever the person works out. The carbs are to be just enough to sustain the person during the workout without having an effect on the ketosis status.

This is actually an SKD plan with the added carbs and workout around three times per week, usually every other day. This diet is suitable for a person who is disciplined enough to exercise.

Cyclical Ketogenic Diet (CKD): This form of the diet calls for the strict version of the diet for five days of the week and binging on carbs on the other two days.

In many cases, you are currently burning glucose as your 'fuel' source, which in turn will change your food into energy. The remainder of the glucose develops into fat and is stored in your body to be consumed at a later time.

The keto diet will set up your body to deplete the stored glucose. Once that is accomplished, your body will focus on diminishing the stored fat you have saved as fuel. Many people don't understand that counting calories don't matter at this point since it is just used as a baseline.

Your body doesn't need glucose which will trigger these two stages:

The State of Glycogenesis: The excess of glucose converts itself into glycogen, which is stored in the liver and muscles. Research studies have indicated that only about half of your energy used daily can be saved as glycogen.

The State of Lipogenesis: This phase is introduced when there is an adequate supply of glycogen in your liver and muscles, with any excess being converted to fat and stored.

Your body will have no more food (much like when you are sleeping), making your body burn the fat to create ketones. Once the ketones break down the fats, which generate fatty acids, they will burn-off in the liver through beta-oxidation. Thus, when you no longer have a supply of glycogen or glucose, ketosis begins and will use the consumed/stored fat as energy.

You will drop the pounds and will also lower your triglycerides, blood pressure, and blood sugar. There's no set rule for carb intake. These are the basic guidelines to consider as you blaze the path on the ketogenic diet plan:

20-50 Grams Each Day: If you have diabetes, are obese, or metabolically deranged, this is the plan for you. Your body will achieve a ketosis state which supplies the ketone bodies.

100-150 Grams Each Day: Stay within these limits if you are active and lean, trying to maintain weight.

How Many Daily Carbs You Require Daily

The Internet provides you with several ways to calculate your daily intake of carbs. Try an easy to follow keto calculator for assistance. Begin your weight loss process by making a habit of checking your ketone levels daily to understand better what essentials your body will need. You'll document your personal information, such as height and weight. The Internet calculator will provide you with essential math.

Knowing When You Are In Ketosis

Thirst is Increased: You counter-balance by increasing your water intake since you can become dehydrated.

Keto Flu/Induction Flu: The diet can make you confused, lethargic, irritable, nauseous, and you may also suffer from a lingering headache. Several days into the plan should remedy these effects. However, you can add 0.5 tsp. of salt to a glass of water and drink it to help with the side effects. You may need to do this once a day for about the first week, and it could take about 15 to 20 minutes after you drink it before it helps.

Digestive Issues: You have made an enormous change in your diet overnight. It's expected that you may have problems, including constipation or diarrhea, when you first start the keto diet. This is yet another reason why you must drink plenty of water.

The low-carbs contribute to the digestive issues. Since each person is different, and it will depend on your chosen diet plan and what foods you have selected to

eat to increase your fiber intake. Try not to introduce new foods into your daily meal regimen until the transitional phase of ketosis is concluded. Digestive issues will improve with time.

Maintain Ketosis Status

You can manage the ketones in your body, whether or not you are on a vegan-keto or a traditional keto.

Each of these methods comes with its advantages and disadvantages. While there may be more ways to measure ketones, these are the three most popular ways:

Consider Using Urine Strips: This is the simplest, easiest, and cheapest method to measure your ketone levels. For most beginners, this is the first option. All you need to do is pee on the stick or dip it in your urine. The color changes 15 seconds later to indicate the presence of ketones or not. A dark purple reading shows that you are in ketosis.

Ketone urine strips are great because they're available at a general pharmacy and are easy on the budget. However, the downside of using urine strips is that it is mostly dependent on the amount of water you drink before you do the test. Because of this, the test doesn't show a precise level of ketones.

Breath Ketone Analyzer Option: An effortless way to measure ketones is by using a breathalyzer. The machines are more expensive than urine strips, costing $150 at the least. However, they are much cheaper than meters. These analyzers are reusable many more times and work using a color code as well, as opposed to giving you a numerical value on the precise ketone level.

Blood Ketone Meter: If you're at an advanced state of ketosis and your body has adapted to it, the blood ketone meter is a worthwhile investment to consider. It will show you the exact levels of ketones found in the blood. The only downside is it is rather expensive. This meter also requires you to prick your finger for a drop of blood to measure your ketones.

Chapter 2: How To Get Into Ketosis

You will achieve the perfect mixture of the traditional keto diet plan of 5% carbs, 25% protein, and fats at 70% ratios. Begin your weight loss process by checking your levels when you want to know what essentials your body needs during your dieting plan. You will document your personal information, such as height and weight. The <u>Internet calculator</u> will provide your numbers to abide by using the dieting plan. Remember to keep in mind; net carbs are the number you are seeking for your daily carb counts. This is the much-needed formula: Total Carbs minus (-) Fiber = Net Carbs. This is the logic used for each of the recipes included in this cookbook and guidelines.

Several plans are available for you as you start the ketogenic journey including, the Standard Ketogenic Diet or SKD requires you to consume low carbs, high amounts of fat, and moderate amounts of protein daily. This method is also excellent for those who have had difficulties losing weight by other means.

You have a Targeted Keto Diet, also called the TKD, which is formatted by the intake of 25 to 50 grams of carbs whenever you are in workout mode. Mostly, TKD is applied for those who are disciplined and do regular exercise or those who have a workout at least three times weekly.

The Cyclical Ketogenic Diet option is referred to as CKD, which is a strict version requiring what is called the 5:2 diet whereby you eat foods from the keto plan for five days and binge the carbs the other two days.

The general guidelines fall with the 20-50 gram allotment for carbs. However, if you are attempting to maintain your weight, and are active and lean, you could consume up to 100-150 carbs daily.

How To Begin Your Ketogenic Path:

Step 1: Choose a time of the day or night during a time when you can relax to begin your new way of eating.

Step 2: Discard all of the non-keto foods from your refrigerator and pantry.

Step 3: Restock the kitchen with keto food items.

Step 4: Consider skipping one meal each day. Maybe sleep a little longer and have brunch. Your meal plan is flexible!

Step 5: Make a routine. Drink a large glass of water and have a supplement of ½ teaspoon of MCT oil or two teaspoons of coconut oil.

Step 6: Keep track of your ketone levels. (More about this in chapter 2.)

Chapter 3: How To Stay In Ketosis

You are probably burning glucose as your primary fuel source since it changes food into energy. The rest of the glucose will develop into fat and be stored. The ketogenic diet is the tool used to deplete the stored glucose. When your body doesn't need the glucose, it will trigger two stages, glycogenesis and lipogenesis.

That excess is converted into glycogen, which is stored or saved in your muscles and liver.

Once the ketones break down the fats, which generate fatty acids, they will burn-off in the liver through beta-oxidation. Thus, when you no longer have a supply of glycogen or glucose, ketosis begins and will use the consumed/stored fat as energy.

The glycerol and fatty acid molecules are released; thus, triggering the ketosis process to begin, whereby acetoacetate is produced. The Acetoacetate is converted to two types of ketone units, acetone, and

BHB. Acetone mostly excreted as waste but can also be metabolized into glucose. This is the reason individuals on a ketogenic diet will experience a distinctive smelly breath. Your muscles will convert the acetoacetate into Beta-hydroxybutyrate or BHB, which will fuel your brain after you have been on the keto diet for a short time.

Know When You Are In Ketosis

There will be some tell-tale signs to let you know for sure that you have reached ketosis. You will experience what is called the keto or induction flu. You may become irritable, a bit confused, lethargic, nauseous, or you may also suffer from a lingering headache. Several days into the plan should remedy these effects. For a quick remedy, add ½ of a teaspoon of salt to a glass of water and drink it to help with the side effects. You may need to do this once a day for about the first week, and it could take about 15 to 20 minutes before it helps.

It's expected that you may have problems, including constipation or diarrhea, when you first start the keto diet. This is yet another reason why you must drink plenty of water. The low-carbs contribute to the digestive issues. Each person is different, and it will depend on your selected diet plan and what foods you have chosen to eat to increase your fiber intake. Try not to introduce new foods into your daily meal regimen until the transitional phase of ketosis is concluded. Digestive issues will improve with time.

You may also be lacking beneficial bacteria. Add fermented foods to your diet plan and increase your probiotics to aid digestion issues. You can benefit from omega 3 fatty acids, B vitamins, and other beneficial enzymes as well. Add a small amount of salt to your food to help with the movements. If all else fails, try a dose of Milk of Magnesia.

The loss of magnesium (a mineral) can be a factor that creates pain with the onset of the keto diet plan changes. With the loss of the minerals during urination, you could experience attacks of cramps in your legs.

You may begin to feel 'fluttery' as a result of dehydration or because of an insufficient intake of salt. Try to adjust your menu plan by trying more carbs. If you don't feel better quickly, you should seek emergency care.

After you have a good night of sleep, your body is in ketosis (since you have fasted for over eight hours); you're well on the way to burning ketones. If you are new to the ketogenic plan (high-fat and low-carb dieting), the optimal fat-burning state takes time. Your body has depended on bringing in carbs and glucose; it will not readily give up carbs and start to crave saturated fats. A restless night is also a typical side effect.

Measure Your State Of Ketosis

Maintaining ketosis is an individual process, and you need to be sure you are achieving your goals. The levels of beta-hydroxybutyrate, acetone, and acetoacetate can be measured in your blood, urine, and breath.

Measure the ketones with a blood ketone meter. All it takes is a small drop of blood on a testing strip inserted into the meter. This process has been researched as an excellent indicator of your current ketosis levels. Unfortunately, the testing strips are expensive.

Test your urine for acetoacetate. The strip is dipped into the urine, which will change the color of the strip. The various shades will indicate the levels of the ketones. A significant benefit is they are inexpensive. The most effective time to test is early in the morning after a ketogenic diet dinner the evening before testing.

You can use a 'Ketonix' meter to measure your breath. You breathe into the meter. The results will be provided by a unique coded color that will flash to show your levels of ketosis at that time.

You should use one or more of these methods to indicate whether you need to adjust your intake of foods to remain in ketosis.

If or when you fast, the hormones in your body will change. The keto plan is similar to this process. You could achieve ketosis in just a couple of days once you have used up all of your stored glycogen. It can take a month. It all depends on which type of plan you choose. Your protein and carbohydrate intake will determine the time.

Chapter 4: Vegan Versus Keto

The foods found in this segment are not allowed on the vegan diet plan. Transitioning from a keto diet to a plant-based vegan-keto lifestyle, the first thing you will need to do is cut out all animal products. Once you've done that, it will be a simple matter of following the food basics of what you should and shouldn't eat.

Vegans "avoid foods containing any ingredients that come from animals."

These are several examples for a better understanding of the process:

- Meat: Wild meat, veal, pork, lamb, organ meat & beef

- Dairy: Milk, butter, cream, cheese, yogurt & ice cream

- Poultry: Chicken, quail, duck goose & turkey

- Eggs: From chickens, quail & fish.

- Bee products: Bee pollen, honey & royal jelly

- Fish & Seafood: All types of fish, lobster, crab, mussels, squid, shrimp, anchovies, calamari, shrimp, scallops, and fish sauce.

Individuals on the keto diet plan can indulge in meat, egg, and cheese options.

Keep these keto foods in mind also:

- Soft and hard cheeses (ex. sharp cheddar or mozzarella)

- Brie Cheese - 0.1 grams - net carbs per 1 oz.

- Colby or Cheddar Cheese - 0.4 net carbs per 1 oz.

- Cottage cheese - 2% fat - 4.1 per .5 cup

- Cottage cheese - creamed - 2.8 per .5 cup

- Heavy whipping cream - double cream - whipped - 3 grams of net carbs per .5 cup

- Cream cheese - 0.8 net carbs per 2 tbsp.

- Sour cream -1 gram net carb per 1 tbsp.

- Feta Cheese - 1.2 grams net carbs per 1 oz.

- Parmesan cheese - 0.9 per 1 oz.

Sugar Options

Swerve Granular Sweetener: This is a super keto-friendly choice and is certified non-GMO, zero net carbs, zero calories, and non-glycemic. It won't raise your blood sugar and measures cup-for-cup just like sugar. It can be purchased in confectioners and granular forms. For convenience, it also is sold in individual packages. It is also an excellent baking option with a composition of natural flavors and erythritol. It carries 0.2 calories per teaspoon, with 60 to 80% of the sweetness of sugar.

Stevia Drops offer delicious flavors, including hazelnut, vanilla, English toffee, and chocolate. Enjoy making a satisfying cup of sweetened coffee or other healthy drinks. For starters, use only three drops to equal one teaspoon of sugar.

Monk Fruit Sweetener: This sweetener is a small green melon used as a natural sweetener that can be used anywhere you would use regular sugar. The monks first cultivated it many centuries ago.

Monk fruit extract contains zero carbs and calories, making it a fantastic option for a ketogenic diet. The amount used can vary between different brands based on what other ingredients may be included in the particular recipe used. It also holds anti-inflammatory properties, promotes weight loss, and is safe for those with diabetes.

Erythritol Powder: Enjoy this as a natural low-calorie sweetener without the added calories. Erythritol is categorized as sugar alcohols, which include maltitol, sorbitol, and xylitol. It contains 70% of the sweetness with 0.24 calories per gram compared to 4 calories in table sugar. However, because of its chemical structure, you may have digestive issues if consumed in large quantities. One of its deeming qualities is that it does not raise your blood sugar levels.

Flour Options

Almond Flour: Prepare a batch of this healthy gluten-free baking by blanching the almonds in a pot of boiling water. Remove the skins. Grind the almonds into a fine flour to use for cooking or baking low-carb cookies, cakes, and pie crusts. Almond flour is a suitable replacement and is used as all-purpose flour. Each ¼ cup portion is only 6 carbs per gram, 150 calories, 3 net carbs, and 11 grams of fat, which makes it an excellent keto-friendly option.

Coconut Flour: Use the coconut option for your keto baking needs, which contains only 3 grams of net carbs and 4 grams of protein for two tablespoons. You can add oils, eggs, and other liquids as needed.

Psyllium Husks: This beneficial item is a form of fiber. It is known as a laxative as well as its benefits to your pancreas and heart. You will see it in some of your bread recipes.

Enjoy these veggies for side dishes:

- Sprouted Alfalfa Seeds (0.2)

- Arugula (2.05)

- Asparagus (6 spears - 2.4)

- Hass Avocado (.5 of 1 - 1.8)

- Bamboo shoots (3)

- Green snap beans (3.6)

- Beet greens (0.63)

- Bell pepper (2.1)

- Broccoli (4.04)

- Savoy cabbage (3)

- Regular size carrots (6.78)

- Baba carrots (5.34)

- Cauliflower (2.97)

- Celery (1.37)

- Chard (2.14)

- Chicory greens (0.7)

- Chives – 1.85)

- Coriander or Cilantro leaves (0.87)

- Cucumber with peel (3.13)

- Eggplant (2.88)

- Garlic (30.96)

- Ginger root (15.77)

- Kale (5.15)

- Leeks – bulb + lower leaf (12.35)

- Red leaf lettuce (1.36)

- Iceberg lettuce (1.77)

- Brown mushrooms (3.7)

- Mustard greens (1.47)

- Yellow onions (7.64)

- Scallions or spring onions (4.74)

- Sweet onions (6.65)

- Banana peppers (1.95)

- Red hot chili peppers (7.31)

- Jalapeno peppers (3.7)

- Sweet green peppers (2.94)

- Sweet red peppers (3.93)

- Sweet yellow peppers (5.42)

- Portabella mushrooms (2.57)

- Pumpkin (6)

- Radishes (1.8)

- Kelp seaweed (8.27)

- Spirulina seaweed (2.02)

- Shiitake mushrooms (4.29)

- Spinach (1.43)

- Crookneck summer squash (2.64)

- Winter acorn squash (8.92)

- Tomatoes (2.69)

- Turnips (4.63)

- Turnip greens (3.93)

- Summer squash (2.6)

- Raw watercress (3.57)

- White mushrooms (2.26)

- Zucchini (1.5)

- List Of Keto Fruits

- It's crucial to eat plenty of fruits while on the ketogenic diet plan. It is much healthier to grab a fruit versus a handful of candy. Enjoy these according to your daily limits of carbohydrates.

- These are some of your best options calculated individually:

- Blackberries: 4 grams per ½ cup

- Blueberries & Raspberries: 3 grams per ½ cup

- Plum: 1 medium-sized is 7 grams

- Strawberries

Chapter 5: Following Vegan Food Guidelines

Stay ahead of the keto game by using a food journal to help you keep track of everything you are eating. Foods on the vegan diet are acceptable as a step up from the keto plan. These are some of the foods you can enjoy.

Fat Resources For The Vegan Diet

Coconut Oil: Versatile uses from roasting veggies to searing tofu or even baking. You vamp up the fat intake with this high flash-point oil. Use it on top of a variety of vegetables. Enjoy a coconut oil smoothie before your workouts. It will quickly transfer from solid form to oil according to its temperature.

Extra-Virgin Olive Oil (EVOO): Olive oil dates back for centuries – back to where oil was used for anointing priests and kings. It's a high-quality oil with low-acidity, making the oil have a smoke point as high as 410º Fahrenheit. That's higher than most cooking applications call for, making olive oil more heat-stable than many other cooking fats. It contains (2 tsp.) -0- carbs.

Monounsaturated fats, such as the ones in olive oil, are also linked with better blood sugar regulation, including lower fasting glucose, as well as reducing inflammation throughout the body. Olive oil also helps to prevent cardiovascular disease by protecting the integrity of your vascular system and lowering LDL, which is also called the 'bad' cholesterol.

Other Monounsaturated & Saturated Fats: Include these items (listed in grams):

- Avocado, Sesame, Olive, & Flaxseed Oil (1 tbsp. - 0- net carbs)
- Olives (3 jumbo - 5 large/10 small – 1 net carb)
- Unsweetened flaked coconut (3 tbsp. – 2 net carbs)

List of Vegan Superfoods

Almonds help to regulate your blood pressure as well as having a good source as an energy booster. Its antioxidant qualities are also loaded with fiber and calcium. Just 0.25 cup of almonds provides eight grams of vegan protein.

Blueberries: The high content of flavonoid antioxidants are what is accountable to have shown enhancement in memory, as well as general cognitive function and learning. The flavonoid categories to stock up on include maqui, acai, and cacao.

Cranberries: The high concentration of ursolic acid helps protect your brain cells from degeneration and injury, possibly even reversing the damage. Choose sun-dried without sugar and use a bit of fruit juice for sweetener or have some of the berries fresh, which is even more nutritious.

Chia Seeds: The rich omega-3 fatty acid content is abundant in the chia seeds, which is linked to helping enhance memory and protect against cognitive decline. You also receive a lower calorie boost.

Strawberries: Not only are these berries loaded with antioxidants, but they are also a good source of vitamin C, along with 21% RDA of manganese. They also help fight cancer.

Pumpkin Seeds: You will receive a boost of zinc, which is linked to the enhancement of your thinking and memory skills. Have some in seasonal soups, by the handful, or in a hearty salad.

Goji Berries: Preliminary studies have indicated the lycopene in the berries is promising for the treatment of Alzheimer's. Have a handful, toss them in with some cereal, or in a tasty smoothie.

Excellent Vegan Spices & Other Goods

Black Pepper: Pepper promotes nutrient absorption in the tissues all over your body, speeds up your metabolism, and improves digestion. The main ingredient of pepper is a pipeline, which gives it the pungent taste. It can boost fat metabolism by as much as 8% for up to several hours after it's ingested.

Basil: This is excellent as a beneficial anti-inflammatory herb. You can use either dried or fresh basil to maximize the benefits. Its dark green color is an indication that it also maintains an outstanding source of calcium, magnesium, and vitamin K (good for your bones). These are some of the conditions it helps:

Cayenne Pepper Hot Spices: Your metabolism will be increased to help burn away the fat. Cayenne is actually a stimulant for digestive enzymes and helps to prevent stomach ulcers. Its anti-inflammatory elements make it a super choice for headaches, arthritis, or sore muscles. You can also receive a boost in your immunity as it clears away nasal congestion. Sprinkle your soups, stews, or chili.

Cumin: This spice is an antioxidant and as an excellent digestion reliever. It is a superior method to treat disorders such as bronchitis and asthma. It is also excellent for prediabetics or diabetes and is also excellent for the removal of body fat. It's an excellent source for vitamins A & C as well as a source for iron.

Turmeric Spices: Dating back to Ayurveda and Chinese medicine - this Asian orange herb has been known for its anti-inflammatory elements. It is so easy to add to your delicious veggies. These are some of its benefits:

- Excellent for weight management
- Improves your digestion
- Relieves arthritis
- Helps control diabetes
- Helps Prevent Alzheimer's disease
- Reduces your cholesterol levels

Nutmeg: You will enhance your foods with the warm, slightly nutty flavor of nutmeg as it is often used in desserts and curries. The nutmeg seeds are

compounds that act as antioxidants in your body. It also carries anti-inflammatory properties to assist in adverse health conditions such as arthritis, diabetes, and heart disease. Nutmeg will also protect you from harmful bacteria, including Streptococcus mutans and E. coli, with its beneficial antibacterial components.

Spicy & Sweet Cloves: Add cloves to hot tea for a spicy change. The germicidal ingredients found in cloves will help with many types of pain.

- The smell of cloves can help encourage mental creativity
- Relief of digestive problems
- Fights infections
- Helps relieve arthritis pain
- Reduces gum and tooth pain

Purchase clove oil which is beneficial as an antiseptic to kill bacteria in fungal infections, itchy rashes, bruises, or burns.

Cinnamon: Use cinnamon as part of your daily plan to improve your insulin receptor activity. Just put one-half of a teaspoon of cinnamon into a smoothie, shake, or any other dessert.

Prepare This Homemade Pumpkin Pie Spice:
- Yields Provided: 10.75 tsp.
- Nutritional Facts Per Serving:
- Protein Count: 0.12 grams
- Total Fat Content: 0.9 grams
- Net Carbohydrates: 0.8 grams
- Calorie Count: 6.4

Ingredients Needed:
- Ground cinnamon (2 tbsp.)
- Ground nutmeg (.5 tsp.)
- Ground ginger (1 tbsp.)
- Allspice (.5 tsp.)
- Cardamom (.25 tsp.)
- Ground cloves (.5 tsp. or .75 tsp. whole cloves)
-

Preparation Method:
1.   Use a spice grinder to grind the cloves into powder.

2.   Combine all of the components into a large mixing container until combined thoroughly.

3.   Store in a spice container to use any time the need arises.

Other Essential Staples:

- Nutritional Yeast: Good to sprinkle on popcorn or potatoes, as well as sauces or tofu coating.
- Vegetable Stock: You can purchase them at the store or make them from scratch.
- Grains: White and brown rice, quinoa, millet, farro, and bulgur
- Ground Flax Seeds: These supply Omega-3 fatty acids

Vegan Substitutes

As you know, eggs can be exchanged with chia seeds, flax seeds, and tofu. Vegetables, whole grains, and fruits are a super choice for a vegan. Choose molasses or maple syrup instead of honey. Dairy products can be replaced with plant milk.

Sugar is another area that you can use substitutions, including natural organic sugar, fructose, beet sugar, date sugar, maple crystals, turbinado sugar, and unbleached cane sugar. The reasoning is because the process involved uses bone char from animals for refinement.

Quinoa: The miracle grain boasts more than 8 grams of protein in each cup. It's one of the only meatless options that contains all of the amino acids that the human body must rely on, which is essential for tissue growth and repair. When taken all together, it's often referred to in certain circles as the world's most perfect protein.

Lentils: They're high protein while packing in 9 grams per half-cup. It has a peppery flavor. It's also a favorite in curries and soups or as a binder for veggie burgers.

Jackfruit: Jackfruit is an excellent substitute for red meat with a texture that is similar to pulled pork or shredded chicken. This is a tropical fruit that can be found in major supermarkets.

Chickpeas: Garbanzo beans or chickpeas are another member of the legume family and rich in fiber and nutrients with little fat. They have more protein than most other legumes at around 12 grams per cup. They're served hot or cold and can be used as a substitute for chicken or tuna on salads. They are also delicious in a dish called hummus. Whip them up using a bit of lemon juice, salt, olive oil, pepper, and paprika and indulge. Add chickpeas to bulk up soups or stews.

Nuts: Cashews, almonds, pine nuts, and pistachios. A bit more about almonds. You can possibly help to regulate your blood pressure as well as having a good source as an energy booster. Its antioxidant qualities are also loaded with fiber and calcium. Just 1/4 of a cup of almonds provides eight grams of vegan protein. Each of these options is shown for 3.5 ounces or 100 grams per serving. A rough guideline is approximately three handfuls. These options do not include any extra toppings such as may be listed as honey roasted, sweet chili, salted caramel, and similar additives. You will consume the carbs quickly as shown:

- 65 pecan halves (4)
- 20 Brazil nuts (4)
- 40 macadamias (5)
- 70 hazelnuts (7)
- 25 walnuts or 50 walnut halves (7)
- 2/3 cup of peanuts (8)
- 80 almonds (9)
- 3/4 cup of pistachios (15)
- 3/4 cup of pine nuts (9)
- 60 cashews (22)

Tahini: Sesame paste works side by side with miso.

Miso: Light and dark paste used soups, dressings, tofu, veggies, and salad

Maple Syrup: As a natural sweetener, it's used for dressing, glazes, and is perfect for baking.

Vegan Meat Options:

Tofu: As an all-time essential in a vegan kitchen, this soy-based protein takes on seasoning so well and can be used in curries and as stuffing or pasta. Tofu is probably the most popular of all meat alternatives. It will substitute for beef, chicken, and pork. This soybean-based product boasts 8 grams of protein for every three ounces of extra-firm tofu.

Preparing tofu for meat-heavy dishes is relatively easy. Just pat dry or wrap the tofu in a kitchen towel with a heavy book over the top to remove excess moisture from the product. Most people will marinate the cubes or slices before sautéing or grilling.

Depending on the destination of the tofu, you can choose from any consistency, from extra-firm to silken. Tofu is purchased in blocks and is an excellent choice to have on hand for your next cooking experience.

Tempeh: You can use tempeh as a protein source that has been around since the 12ty century. It's readily available in a variety of brands, packing 31 grams of protein per cup with a mild and nutty flavor that works great with many recipes.

Seitan: Wheat gluten is another term used for seitan and has been used in Asian cuisine since the sixth century. The dense meat devours your spices and is protein-packed with 60 grams per cup as a low-carb and cholesterol-free option for vegan cooking needs.

Vegan Nutritional Benefits

Potassium: Acidity and water are balanced by potassium, which also leads to a reduction in cancer and cardiovascular diseases.

Protein: Red meat is not necessarily the healthiest choice for protein. As a vegan, lentils, nuts, peas, beans, and soy products provide this resource without health issues.

Fiber: The vegans experience better bowel movements with the increased high fiber in veggies and fruits.

Antioxidants: With this addition, you can protect your body against several types of cancer.
Reduced Saturated Fats: Without the meats and dairy products, these levels are lowered immensely.

Magnesium: With the assistance of magnesium, calcium is better absorbed. It is found in dark leafy greens, seeds, and nuts.

Vitamin C: The C vitamin works as an antioxidant and helps your bruises heal faster and keeps your gums healthy.

Other Benefits
- Inflammatory bowel conditions
- Allergies
- Arthritis
- Weight Loss
- Lowered risk for cardiovascular disease

- Blood pressure
- Type 2 Diabetes
- Bone health such as osteoporosis
- Many forms of cancer

Chapter 6 : Keto-Friendly Sauces & Condiments

Alfredo Sauce

Yields Provided: 4

Nutritional Facts Per Serving:

- **Protein Count**: 2.9 grams
- **Total Fat Content**: 18 grams
- **Net Carbohydrates**: 3.2 grams
- **Calorie Count**: 176

Ingredients Needed:

- Vegan butter (3 tbsp.)
- Garlic (5 cloves)
- Vegan mayo (1 tbsp.)
- Nutritional yeast (2 tbsp.)
- Optional: Almond flour (2 tbsp.)
- Coconut milk (14 oz.)
- Black pepper and salt (as desired)

Preparation Method:

1. Melt the butter in a saucepan.

2. Mince the garlic and sauté in the prepared pan for two minutes, adding the flour for thickening as needed.

3. Mix in the remainder of the fixings. Simmer and stir well.

4. Use the low-temperature setting for five minutes until thickened to your liking.

5. Serve over zoodles, pasta, or veggies.

Asian Hoisin Sauce

Yields Provided: 8

Nutritional Facts Per Serving:

- **Protein Count**: 3 grams
- **Total Fat Content**: 5 grams
- **Net Carbohydrates**: 2 grams
- **Calorie Count**: 71

Ingredients Needed:

- Tamari (4 tbsp.)
- Natural/organic smooth peanut butter (2 tbsp.)
- Rice wine vinegar (2 tsp.)
- Garlic clove (1)
- Frank's Hot Sauce (1 tsp.)
- Pepper (1 pinch)

- Sesame oil (3 tsp.)
- Chinese five-spice (.25 tsp.)
- Xanthan gum (.125 tsp.)
- Sugar-free maple syrup (2 tsp.)

Preparation Method:

1. Toss all of the fixings into a blender.
2. Mix well until the sauce has thickened (2-3 min.)
3. It will keep in the refrigerator for up to three weeks.

Avocado Mayonnaise

Yields Provided: 4

Nutritional Facts Per Serving:

- **Protein Count**: 1 gram
- **Total Fat Content**: 5 grams
- **Net Carbohydrates**: 1 gram

Ingredients Needed:

- Ground cayenne pepper (.5 tsp.)
- Pinch of pink salt (1 pinch)
- Lime for juice (.5 of 1)
- Medium avocado (.5 of 1)
- Olive oil (.25 cup)
- *Also Needed*: Blender or food processor

Preparation Method:

1. Dice the avocado. Combine the salt, cayenne, cilantro, avocado, and lime juice in the blender.
2. When smooth, stir in the oil - 1 tablespoon at a time - pulsing in between each addition.
3. Store the mayo for up to seven days in a sealed glass bottle in the fridge.

Basil - Pesto Sauce

Yields Provided: 4

Nutritional Facts Per Serving:

- **Protein Count**: 6 grams
- **Total Fat Content**: 29 grams
- **Net Carbohydrates**: 2 grams
- **Calorie Count**: 281

Ingredients Needed:

- Pine nuts (.33 cup)
- Fresh basil leaves (2 cups)
- Garlic clove (1)
- Vegan grated parmesan cheese (3 tbsp.)
- Olive oil (.33 cup or as needed)
- Salt and black pepper (as desired)

Preparation Method:

1. Pulse the pine nuts, garlic, basil, and parmesan in a blender or food processor until it's all chopped.
2. Slowly pour in the oil with the machine running, mixing until the pesto has thickened.
3. Adjust the consistency using oil, and season with pepper and salt.

Cashew Pesto

Yields Provided:1.25 cup (.25 cup each)

Nutritional Facts Per Serving:

- **Protein Count**: 8 grams
- **Total Fat Content**:19 grams
- **Net Carbohydrates**: 4.3 grams
- **Calorie Count**: 241

Ingredients Needed:

- Basil (1 cup packed)
- Raw cashews (.5 cup)
- Olive oil (.33 cup)
- Nutritional yeast (3 tbsp.)
- Apple cider vinegar (2 tbsp.)
- Black pepper (.25 tsp.)

- Pink salt (as desired)
- Garlic powder (.5 tsp.) or Garlic cloves (4)

Preparation Method:

1. Mix each of the fixings in a blender or food processor - omitting the salt.
2. Blend well until creamy and add salt to your liking.

Cheese Sauce

Yields Provided: 10

Nutritional Facts Per Serving:

- **Protein Count**: 6 grams
- **Total Fat Content**: 39 grams
- **Net Carbohydrates**: 2 grams
- **Calorie Count**: 389

Ingredients Needed:

- Vegan cream cheese (8 oz.)
- Vegan mozzarella cheese (2 cups)
- Vegan heavy cream (1 cup)
- Butter (1 cup)

Preparation Method:

1. Combine the cream cheese, butter, and heavy cream in a saucepan using the low heat setting.

2. Stir until the mixture is melted, mixing the mozzarella until it's thoroughly combined.

3. Serve now or store for later.

Marinara Sauce

Yields Provided: 4 cups

Nutritional Facts Per Serving:

- **Protein Count**: 1 gram
- **Total Fat Content**: 7 grams
- **Net Carbohydrates**: 3 grams
- **Calorie Count**: 84

Ingredients Needed:

- Peeled tomatoes - no sugar added (28 oz. can)
- Olive oil (.25 cup)
- Red wine vinegar (1 tbsp.)
- Black pepper (.25 tsp)
- Garlic powder (1 tsp.)
- Dried basil (1 tsp.)
- Salt (1 tsp.)
- Dried parsley (1 tsp.)
- Onion powder (1 tsp.)
- Dried oregano (1 tsp.)
- Red pepper flakes (.5 tsp.)

Preparation Method:

1. In a small blender, puree the olive oil, tomatoes, and ½ cup of liquid from the can.

2. Stir in the rest of the fixings. Taste and season as desired.

Parmesan Cheese - Vegan

Yields Provided: 16

Nutritional Facts Per Serving:

- **Protein Count**: 1.8 grams
- **Total Fat Content**: 3 grams
- **Net Carbohydrates**: 2.3 grams

Ingredients Needed:

- Nutritional yeast (3 tbsp.)
- Garlic powder (.25 tsp.)
- Raw cashews (.75 cup)
- Sea salt (.75 tsp.)

Preparation Method:

1. Toss all of the fixings into a food processor.

2. Pulse until it's an ultra-fine meal.

3. Store in the refrigerator for two or three weeks.

Vegan Sour Cream

Yields Provided: 16 - 2 tbsp. per serving

Nutritional Facts Per Serving:

- **Protein Count**: 2 grams
- **Total Fat Content**: 4 grams
- **Net Carbohydrates**: 3 grams
- **Calorie Count**: 56

Ingredients Needed:

- Water (1 cup)
- Raw cashews (1.25 cups)
- Probiotic capsules (2-3) **
- Lemon juice (1 tbsp.)
- Sea salt (.25 tsp.)
- Apple cider vinegar (1 tsp.)

Preparation Method:

1. Prepare a pot of hot water. Soak the cashews for one hour or use cold water and soak for six hours to overnight. When ready, drain them in a colander.
2. Dump the soaked cashews into a high-speed blender with water. Mix well until smooth. Scoop the mixture into a mixing bowl.
3. Open and empty the contents of each capsule

into the mixture, and stir with a wooden spoon.

4. Use a layer of cheesecloth to cover and close securely using a rubber band.

5. Let it rest on the countertop, warmer than 70° Fahrenheit, for 24-48 hours. *Note*: The longer it rests, the thicker and tangier it becomes.

6. Once the mixture has reached your preferred tanginess and texture, uncover and add the salt, lemon juice, and apple cider vinegar. Mix well.

7. Chill for a minimum of six hours.

8. *Note*: **One probiotic capsule (emptied) should measure about ⅓ of a teaspoon of the probiotic powder used in the recipe.

Worcestershire Sauce

Yields Provided: 12

Nutritional Facts Per Serving:
- **Protein Count**: 0.5 grams
- **Total Fat Content**: 0.1 grams
- **Net Carbohydrates**: 0.8 grams
- **Calorie Count**: 7.7

Ingredients Needed:
- Soy sauce/liquid coconut aminos
- Water (4 tbsp.)

- White/Apple cider vinegar (3 tbsp.)
- Garlic powder (1 tsp.)
- Onion powder (1 tsp.)
- Ground cinnamon (1 tsp.)
- Mustard powder (1 tsp.)
- Ground black pepper (.5 tsp.)
- Plain/smoked paprika (2 tsp.)

Preparation Method:

1. Toss all of the fixings into a NutriBullet type blender or use a stick immersion blender until all of the fixings are mixed well.
2. Pour the mixture into a saucepan to simmer using low-medium heat for five to seven minutes.
3. Cool and store in the refrigerator for up to two weeks.

Chapter 7: Breakfast & Brunch Favorites

Eggy Vegan Tofu Scramble

Yields Provided: 2

Nutritional Facts Per Serving:

- **Protein Count**: 20.3 grams
- **Total Fat Content**: 13.1 grams
- **Net Carbohydrates**: 2.9 grams
- **Calorie Count**: 206

Ingredients Needed:

- Extra-firm tofu (8 oz.)
- Vegan butter (1 tbsp.)
- Nutritional yeast (2 tbsp.)
- Turmeric (.5 tsp.)
- Paprika (.5 tsp.)
- Dijon mustard (1 tsp.)
- Garlic powder (.5 tsp.)
- Black salt (Kala Namak* (.25 tsp.)
- Onion powder (.25 tsp.)
- Soy milk (.33 cup)

For Serving:

- Chopped chives
- Fried tomatoes
- Black pepper
- Sliced avocado

Preparation Method:

1. Mash the tofu with a fork, leaving some big chunks.

2. Add the garlic powder, turmeric, nutritional yeast, paprika, dijon mustard, black salt, and onion powder into a mixing bowl. Pour in the soy milk and whisk into a sauce.

3. Add the vegan butter to a skillet and heat until hot. Toss in the tofu and fry it until lightly browned, trying not to break it up too much when moving it around the pan.

4. Mix in the sauce. Fry it until you've achieved desired consistency. The tofu will absorb the sauce, so you can have it as wet or as dry as you like.

5. Top with a portion of black pepper and chopped chives. Serve with fried tomatoes and sliced avocado.

Keto Vegan Bagels - Gluten-Free & Nut-Free

Yields Provided: 6 bagel thins

Nutritional Facts Per Serving:

- **Protein Count**: 6.6 grams
- **Total Fat Content**: 16.4 grams
- **Net Carbohydrates**: 2 grams
- **Calorie Count**: 209

Ingredients Needed:

- Ground flaxseed (.5 cup)
- Tahini (.5 cup)
- Psyllium husks (.25 cup)
- Water (1 cup)
- Baking powder (1 tsp.)
- Salt (1 pinch) add up to 1 tsp. if using unsalted tahini
- *Optional:* Sesame seeds - for garnish

Preparation Method:

1. Warm the oven to reach 375° Fahrenheit.
2. Mix the ground flaxseeds, psyllium husk, baking powder, and salt. Whisk until thoroughly combined.

3. Pour the water into the tahini, whisking until combined.

4. Stir the dry fixings into the wet. Knead to form the dough until it's uniform.

5. Shape the mixture into patties by hand (4 inches in diameter and ¼-inch thick). Spread them onto the baking tray. Cut a small circle from the middle of each round.

6. Add the sesame seeds. Bake for 40 minutes, or until it's golden brown.

7. To enjoy, slice in half, and toast. Then top as desired.

Pancakes - French Toast - Waffles & More

Lemon Waffles - Vegan

Yields Provided: 4

Nutritional Facts Per Serving:

- **Protein Count**: 1.1 grams
- **Total Fat Content**: 8 grams
- **Net Carbohydrates**: 2 grams
- **Calorie Count**: 99

Ingredients Needed:

- Coconut oil (1.5 tbsp.)
- Whole psyllium husks (1 tbsp.)
- Granulated sweetener (1 tbsp.)
- Coconut flour (.25 cup)
- Baking powder (.5 tsp.)
- Salt (1 pinch)
- Lemon juice (1 tbsp.)
- Nondairy milk of choice (5 tbsp.)
- Vanilla extract (.5 tsp.)

Preparation Method:

1. Warm a cast-iron pan using the med-low heat setting.
2. Grease the pan with coconut oil as needed.
3. Whisk the coconut flour, baking powder, psyllium, and salt.
4. Combine with the rest of the fixings in another container.
5. Gently fold in all of the dry fixings into the wet ones until thoroughly mixed. Wait a few minutes until a stiff dough is formed (3-5 min.). Prepare using your hands.

6. Tip: If the coconut oil and psyllium do not absorb enough liquid to form the dough, stir in an additional tablespoon of coconut flour.
7. Portion the dough into four balls. Flatten the balls and cook for approximately five minutes per side or until golden.
8. Let cool for a minute or two before topping.

Cereal Options

Blueberry Overnight Oatmeal - Vegan

Yields Provided: 1

Nutritional Facts Per Serving:

- **Protein Count**: 8 grams
- **Total Fat Content**: 17 grams
- **Net Carbohydrates**: 2 grams
- **Calorie Count**: 275

Ingredients Needed:

- Vegan oatmeal - ex. *Coconut Oatmeal* - see the recipe *below* (1 serving)
- Blueberries (.25 cup)
- Sugar-free blueberry jam (2 tbsp.)
- *Optional:*

- Chia seeds
- Blueberry breakfast cake (enough for 1 serving)

Preparation Method:

1. Prepare the keto oatmeal base as directed.
2. Add in half the blueberries, 1 tablespoon of blueberry jam, and other add-ins of choice. Stir well. Refrigerate overnight.
3. Once you're ready to eat, just add extra milk to reach the desired texture. Garnish using the remainder of the fixings and serve.
4. *Note:* You can adjust the texture by using a little extra water if it's too thick or a few additional chia seeds for thickening.

Coconut Oatmeal - Vegan

Yields Provided: 1

Nutritional Facts Per Serving:

- **Protein Count**: 8 grams
- **Total Fat Content**: 17 grams
- **Net Carbohydrates**: 1 gram
- **Calorie Count**: 250

Ingredients Needed:

- Ground flaxseed (2 tbsp.)

- Chia seeds (2 tbsp.)
- Granulated sweetener of choice (2 tbsp.)
- Hot liquid of choice (.5 cup)
- Cold liquid of choice - unsweetened coconut milk (.5 cup)
- Unsweetened shredded coconut (2 tbsp.)

Preparation Method:

1. Combine each of the dry fixings. Whisk well.
2. Add hot water or another liquid of choice and mix well; the mixture should be super thick. Add the chosen cold liquid and mix until it's thick, creamy 'oatmeal.'
3. Add toppings/mix-ins of choice.

Muesli Cereal

Yields Provided: 15

Nutritional Facts Per Serving:

- **Protein Count**: 8 grams
- **Total Fat Content**: 19 grams
- **Net Carbohydrates**: 3 grams
- **Calorie Count**: 217

Ingredients Needed:

- Cinnamon (2 tsp.)
- Vanilla extract (.5 tsp.)
- SweetLeaf Stevia Drops or vanilla stevia drops (.25 tsp.)
- Sunflower seeds (1 cup)
- Flaked coconut - unsweetened (1 cup)
- Pumpkin seeds (1 cup)
- Hemp hearts (.5 cup)
- Sliced almonds (1 cup)
- Pecans (.5 cup)

Preparation Method:

1. Stir all of the fixings until well mixed.
2. Prepare in a rimmed baking sheet using a layer of parchment baking paper.
3. Bake the mixture at 350° Fahrenheit for 7 to 8 minutes.
4. Cool slightly before serving.

Chapter 8: Salad & Soup Specialties

Salad Options

Asian Zucchini Salad

Yields Provided: 1

Nutritional Facts Per Serving:

- **Protein Count**:14 grams
- **Total Fat Content**: 86 grams
- **Net Carbohydrates**: 7 grams
- **Calorie Count**: 846

Ingredients Needed:

- Medium zucchini (1)
- Shredded cabbage (.5 cup)
- Sunflower seeds (1.5 tbsp.)
- Almonds (.5 tbsp.)
- Sesame oil (1.5 tbsp.)
- White vinegar (1 tbsp.)
- Vegan crumbled feta cheese (.5 cup)

Preparation Method:

1. Roast the almonds in a deep frying pan using the low-temperature setting.
2. Use a spiralizer to shred the zucchini into strips.
3. Prepare the salad using the cabbage, zucchini, almonds, and sunflower seeds.
4. Whisk both oils and the vinegar. Spritz over the salad.
5. Garnish with the feta and toss before serving.

Cauliflower Tabbouleh - Instant Pot

Yields Provided: 4

Nutritional Facts Per Serving:

- **Protein Count**: 4.9 grams
- **Total Fat Content**: 7.1 grams
- **Net Carbohydrates**: 6.8 grams
- **Calorie Count**: 128

Ingredients Needed:

- Cauliflower (1 large head)
- Garlic (1 clove)
- Scallions (.33 cup)
- Tomatoes (.75 cup)

- Fresh parsley (.33 cup)
- Fresh mint (.33 cup)
- Salt & black pepper (as desired)
- Lemon juice (.25 cup)
- Olive oil (2 tbsp.)

Preparation Method:

1. Mince the garlic, scallions, and tomatoes. Slice the cauliflower into florets. Chop the mint and parsley.
2. Pulse the cauliflower florets in a blender or food processor for about 10 seconds to form the rice bits.
3. Transfer the rice into a mixing container and add the lemon juice, olive oil, and garlic. Add the mint, parsley, tomatoes, scallions, salt, and pepper; mix well.
4. Serve right away or refrigerate for a few hours for the best flavor.

Crunchy Cauliflower & Pine Nut Salad

Yields Provided: 1

Nutritional Facts Per Serving:

- **Protein Count**: 10 grams
- **Total Fat Content**: 63 grams
- **Net Carbohydrates**: 8 grams
- **Calorie Count**: 638

Ingredients Needed:

- Cauliflower (.25 cup)
- Onion leeks (2 tbsp.)
- Pine nuts (.25 cup)
- Sour cream (2 tbsp.)
- Iceberg lettuce (.5 cup)
- Vegan mayonnaise (.25 cup)
- Vegan feta cheese (.25 cup)

Preparation Method:

1. Toast the pine nuts using the medium heat temperature setting.
2. Chop the onion, cauliflower, and pine nuts. Shred the lettuce.
3. Combine all of the fixings in a large container and place it in the fridge for a minimum of two hours.
4. Serve cold.

Ginger Walnut & Hemp Seed Lettuce Wraps

Yields Provided: 4

Nutritional Facts Per Serving:

- **Protein Count**: 14 grams
- **Total Fat Content**: 31 grams
- **Net Carbohydrates**: 10 grams
- **Calorie Count**: 382

Ingredients Needed:

The Sauce:

- Low-sodium tamari (2 tbsp.)
- Maple syrup (1 tbsp.)
- Brown rice vinegar (2 tbsp.)
- Minced ginger (1 tbsp.)
- Toasted sesame oil (1 tsp.)

The Filling:

- Hemp seeds (.5 cup)
- Walnuts (1 cup)
- Dates (2)
- Cucumber (.5 cup)
- Carrots (.25 cup)
- Lettuce leaves
- *Optional:* Sesame seeds

Preparation Method:

1. Combine the sauce fixings and set aside.
2. Chop the carrots, cucumbers, dates, and walnuts.
3. Toss the sauce with the rest of the fixings (omit the lettuce) Place in the refrigerator to chill for one hour.
4. Remove and pile onto the lettuce leaves and top off with the seeds to your liking.

Instant Pot Cauliflower & Rice Salad

Yields Provided: 4

Nutritional Facts Per Serving:

- **Protein Count**: 2 grams
- **Total Fat Content**: 7 grams
- **Net Carbohydrates**: 1 gram
- **Calorie Count**: 177

Ingredients Needed:

The Salad:

- Small cauliflower (1 - divided)
- Small Romanesco cauliflower (1 - divided)
- Broccoli (1 lb.)
- Seedless oranges (2)

The Vinaigrette:

- Orange juice & zest (1)
- Salted – unrinsed capers (1 tbsp.)
- Finely chopped hot pepper (1)
- Pepper and salt (as desired)
- Olive oil (4 tbsp.)

Preparation Method:

1. Cut the cauliflower into florets. Remove the peel and thinly slice the oranges. Finely chop the capers, and hot peppers for the vinaigrette.
2. Prepare the vinaigrette fixings in a jar with a lid. Shake well and set aside.
3. Prepare the Instant Pot with one cup of water and the steamer basket. Add the cauliflower to the basket and secure the lid.
4. Set the timer for 6 minutes using low pressure. Quick-release the steam pressure when you hear the timer buzzer.
5. Transfer the florets to a serving dish with the prepared oranges. Toss well and drizzle with the vinaigrette and serve.

Spicy Asian Cucumber Salad

Yields Provided: 2

Nutritional Facts Per Serving:

- **Protein Count**: 1 gram
- **Total Fat Content**: 15 grams
- **Net Carbohydrates**: 7.5 grams
- **Calorie Count**: 170

Ingredients Needed:

- Cucumber (1 large/14 oz.)
- Scallions (2)
- *The Dressing*:
- Low-sodium soy sauce/Bragg Aminos (2 tbsp.)
- Sesame oil (2 tbsp.)
- Rice vinegar (1 tbsp.)
- Sesame seeds (.5 tsp.)
- Crushed red pepper flakes (.5 tsp.)
- Salt and pepper (to your liking)

Preparation Method:

1. Slice the cucumber into coins, then into small wedges. Thinly slice the scallions. Set aside for now.
2. Combine each of the dressing fixings in a small

mixing container. Stir until well-incorporated, adding salt and pepper to taste.

3. In a large salad bowl, toss the cucumbers and scallions with the dressing.

4. Refrigerate the salad for 30 minutes to chill and let the flavors combine. Toss the salad again with the dressing accumulated at the bottom of the bowl, and serve cold.

Soups

Cashew Cheddar Tomato Soup

Yields Provided: 4

Nutritional Facts Per Serving:

- **Protein Count**: 9 grams
- **Total Fat Content**: 26 grams
- **Net Carbohydrates**: 8.75 grams
- **Calorie Count**: 302

Ingredients Needed:

- Minced garlic (1 tsp.)
- Tomato paste (1 small can)
- Oregano (1 tsp.)
- Heavy whipping cream (1 cup)

- Water (.25 cup)
- Black pepper and salt (to your liking)
- Vegan cashew cheddar cheese/see recipe (.75 cup)

Preparation Method:

1. Pour the minced garlic and tomato paste in a dutch oven and add the cream. Gently whisk.
2. As it begins to boil, blend in small amounts of cheese. Pour in the water and simmer four to five minutes.
3. Serve with pepper as desired.

Avocado Mint Chilled Soup

Yields Provided: 2

Nutritional Facts Per Serving:

- **Protein Count**: 4 grams
- **Total Fat Content**: 26 grams
- **Net Carbohydrates**: 4 grams
- **Calorie Count**: 280

Ingredients Needed:

- Romaine lettuce (2 leaves)
- Ripened avocado (1 medium)

- Coconut milk (1 cup)
- Lime juice (1 tbsp.)
- Fresh mint (20 leaves)
- Salt (to your liking)

Preparation Method:

1. Combine all of the fixings into a blender and mix well. You want it thick but not puree-like.
2. Chill in the refrigerator for 5-10 minutes before serving.

Greens Soup

Yields Provided: 6

Nutritional Facts Per Serving:

- **Protein Count**: 6 grams
- **Total Fat Content**: 8 grams
- **Net Carbohydrates**: 6 grams
- **Calorie Count**: 191

Ingredients Needed:

- Spinach leaves (2 cups)
- Diced avocado (1)

- Diced English cucumber (.5 cup)
- Gluten-free vegetable broth (.25 cup)
- Black pepper and salt (to your liking)

Preparation Method:

1. Mix each of the fixings in the blender.
2. Toss in the fresh herbs and serve.

Pomodoro Soup - Instant Pot - Vegan

Yields Provided: 8

Nutritional Facts Per Serving:

- **Protein Count**: 11 grams
- **Total Fat Content**: 18 grams
- **Net Carbohydrates**: 6.5 grams
- **Calorie Count**: 300

Ingredients Needed:

- Coconut cream (1 cup)
- Veggie broth (29 oz.)
- Tomatoes (3 lb.)
- Diced onion (1)
- Vegan butter (3 tbsp.)

Preparation Method:

1. Set the Instant Pot using the sauté mode. Once it's hot, add the butter to melt and toss in the onions. Saute for 3-5 minutes.

2. Mix in the tomatoes and simmer for another 2 minutes. Secure the lid and set the soup function for 6 minutes.

3. Press the cancel button and wait for about 4-5 minutes before you do a quick pressure release. Stir in coconut cream to saute for 1 minute.

Puree the soup using a hand mixer before serving.

Chapter 9: Dinner Options

Brussels Sprouts Spaghetti - Vegan

Yields Provided: 1

Nutritional Facts Per Serving:

- **Protein Count**: 7 grams
- **Total Fat Content**: 23.4 grams
- **Net Carbohydrates**: 5.1 grams
- **Calorie Count**: 259

Ingredients Needed:

- Shirataki noodles (1 pkg.)
- Brussels sprouts (.25 cup)
- Garlic (1 clove)
- Vegan cream cheese (2 tbsp.)
- Olive oil (1 tbsp.)
- Nutritional yeast (1 tbsp.)
- Salt and pepper (as desired)

Preparation Method:

1. Pour the oil into a skillet to get hot.

2. Shred the brussels sprouts and add to the pan with the garlic. Sauté to soften for a few minutes.
3. Rinse and drain the noodles and combine with the rest of the fixings.
4. Stir every few minutes until it's creamy, only adding small amounts of water (no more than 1 tbsp.) at a time.
5. Combine well and serve.

Cauliflower Patties - Instant Pot - Vegan

Yields Provided: 4

Nutritional Facts Per Serving:

- **Protein Count**: 2.8 grams
- **Total Fat Content**: 7 grams
- **Net Carbohydrates**: 2.7 grams
- **Calorie Count**: 120

Ingredients Needed:

- Water (1.5 cups)
- Cauliflower (1 head)
- Vegan cheese (1 cup)
- Ground almonds (1 cup)
- Olive oil (3 tbsp.)

Preparation Method:

1. Empty the water into the cooker. Chop and add the cauliflower into the steamer basket.
2. Secure the top and prepare using the high-pressure setting for 5 minutes. Quick-release the pressure when it's done.
3. Drain the cauliflower and add to a processor to grind down. Shred the cheese and stir in the almonds to make the patties.
4. Heat 1 ½ tablespoons of the oil in the Instant Pot using the sauté function.
5. Brown and repeat in one more batch making sure it's done. Serve.

Garlic Spaghetti Squash - Vegan

Yields Provided: 4

Nutritional Facts Per Serving:

- **Protein Count**: 3 grams
- **Total Fat Content**: 7 grams
- **Net Carbohydrates**: 5.5 grams
- **Calorie Count**: 91

Ingredients Needed:

- Spaghetti squash (1 large - about 4 cups cooked)
- Olive oil (2 tbsp.)
- Garlic powder (1 tsp.) or Minced cloves (2)
- Dried rosemary (1 tsp.)
- Dried thyme (1 tsp.)
- Dried parsley (1 tsp.)
- Sage (.5 tsp.)
- Salt (1 tsp.)
- Freshly cracked pepper (.5 tsp.)

Preparation Method:

1. Warm the oven at 350° Fahrenheit.
2. Split the squash and discard the seeds. Arrange the squash - facedown in a roasting pan. Add small amounts of water in the bottom to steam the squash.
3. Roast for 45 minutes to one hour, until entirely done.
4. Remove the dish from the oven to cool.
5. Scrape out the flesh. Mix with salt, spices, and oil until everything is thoroughly combined.
6. Bake for another 15 minutes to remove the extra moisture.

Keto Lo Mein - Vegan

Yields Provided: 1 large

Nutritional Facts Per Serving:

- **Protein Count**: 5.1 grams
- **Total Fat Content**: 13.9 grams
- **Net Carbohydrates**: 4.4 grams
- **Calorie Count**: 195

Ingredients Needed:

- Kelp noodles (1 pkg.)
- Shredded carrots (2 tbsp.)
- Frozen broccoli (1 cup)
- *For the Sauce*:
- Tamari (2 tbsp.)
- Sesame oil (1 tbsp.)
- Garlic powder (.5 tsp.)
- Ground ginger (.5 tsp.)
- Sriracha/your preference chili pepper (.25 tsp.)

Preparation Method:

1. Open the noodles to soak them in water.

2. In a saucepan, using the med-low heat setting, toss in each of the sauce fixings, and the broccoli.
3. Drain the noodles. Once the pan is hot, add the noodles and cover.
4. Simmer for a few minutes, occasionally stirring the noodles. Mix in a few tablespoons of water as needed.
5. Once the noodles have softened, mix everything until ingredients are well-distributed.
6. Extinguish the heat, and leave the noodles in the pan until all the liquid in the bottom has been absorbed before serving.

Mini-Vegan Shepherd's Pie - Instant Pot

Yields Provided: 4

Nutritional Facts Per Serving:
- **Protein Count**: 12 grams
- **Total Fat Content**: 14 grams
- **Net Carbohydrates**: 4.7 grams
- **Calorie Count**: 225

Ingredients Needed:

- Water (1.5 cups)
- Cauliflower (2 cups)
- Diced onion (1 cup)
- Grated potatoes (1 cup)
- Diced tomatoes (1 cup)

Preparation Method:

1. Steam and mash the cauliflower.
2. Use the sauté function to warm the Instant Pot, adding a splash of water. Toss in the onions. Cook slowly for two minutes.
3. Grate the potatoes and add to the mix and saute for five more minutes. Pour in the tomatoes and continue sauteing for three additional minutes.
4. Prepare each of the ramekins with a spritz of cooking oil spray. Portion the fixings and top it off with the mashed potatoes.
5. Add the water and the trivet into the cooker and secure the lid.
6. Set the timer for 5 minutes on the high setting.
7. Serve when the time is up after a 10-minute natural-release of the pressure.

Mixed Vegetable Vegan Patties - Instant Pot

Yields Provided: 4

Nutritional Facts Per Serving:

- **Protein Count**: 4 grams
- **Total Fat Content**: 10 grams
- **Net Carbohydrates**: 3 grams
- **Calorie Count**: 220

Ingredients Needed:

- Cauliflower florets (1 cup)
- Mixed vegetables - frozen bag (1)
- Water (1.5 cups)
- Flax meal (1 cup)
- Olive oil (2 tbsp.)

Preparation Method:

1. Fill the Instant Pot with the water and add the veggies to the steamer basket.
2. Secure the lid and set the timer for 4 to 5 minutes using high pressure.
3. Quick-release the pressure and drain once the time has elapsed.
4. Use a potato masher and stir in the flax meal. Shape into four patties.

5. Select the sauté function in a clean pot and pour in the oil. Prepare the patties for about three minutes on each side until they are golden brown.

Peanut Ginger Cold Noodle Vegan Salad

Yields Provided: 2

Nutritional Facts Per Serving:

- **Protein Count**: 10.1 grams
- **Total Fat Content**: 16.2 grams
- **Net Carbohydrates**: 7.5 grams
- **Calorie Count**: 214

Ingredients Needed:

- Unsweetened peanut butter (.25 cup)
- Water (.25 cup)
- Low-sodium tamari (1 tbsp.)
- Garlic (1 clove)
- Fresh ginger (1 tsp.)
- Zucchini noodles (2 medium-sized zucchinis)
- *Optional garnishes:*
- Scallions
- Chopped peanuts
- Red pepper flakes

Preparation Method:

1. Grate or mince the garlic and ginger. Whisk the water, tamari, garlic, peanut butter, and ginger. If it's too thick, continue to mix in water until it reaches the desired texture - at the rate of one tablespoon at a time.
2. Toss the sauce in with the noodles.
3. Portion into salad bowls and garnish as desired.

Ramen Vegan Noodles

Yields Provided: 1

Nutritional Facts Per Serving:

- **Protein Count**: 16.5 grams
- **Total Fat Content**: 18.9 grams
- **Net Carbohydrates**: 7 grams
- **Calorie Count**: 283.3

Ingredients Needed:

- *Noodles and Broth:*
- Sesame or olive oil (1 tbsp.)
- Tamari or coconut aminos (2 tbsp.)
- Veggie stock or bouillon and water (2 cups)
- Garlic clove (1 minced)

- Grated ginger (.125 tsp.)
- Shirataki noodles (1 pkg.)
- *The Toppings:*
- Baked or fried tofu (¼ of a block)
- Baby spinach & Sprouts (1 handful each)
- Mixed mushrooms (.25 cup)
- *The Garnish:*
- Seaweed flakes
- Sesame seeds
- Chili flakes
- Chopped scallion

Preparation Method:

1. Gather the ingredients. Sauté the mushrooms and bake the tofu, as needed. (Cube the tofu and marinate it in tamari. Bake for 30 minutes.)
2. Pour the oil into a saucepan using med-low heat. Toss in the garlic, ginger, and aminos/tamari. Sauté for a few minutes until everything smells delicious.
3. Drain and rinse noodles. Mix into the broth, and simmer for five to ten minutes.

4. Transfer the noodles from the broth using a spaghetti spoon or fork and place it at the bottom of the bowl. Add the chosen toppings over the noodles.

5. Carefully, pour broth over the toppings. Garnish with your choice of extra toppings.

Vegan-Inspired Sloppy Joes

Yields Provided: 6

Nutritional Facts Per Serving:

- **Protein Count**: 14.7 grams
- **Total Fat Content**: 29.9 grams
- **Net Carbohydrates**: 8.9 grams
- **Calorie Count**: 354

Ingredients Needed:

- Hulled hemp seeds (.5 cup)
- Pepitas - hulled pumpkin seeds (1 cup)
- Chopped walnuts (1 cup)
- Tomato paste (6 oz.)
- Garlic powder (.5 tbsp.)
- Onion powder (1 tsp.)
- Prepared mustard (1 tbsp.)
- Apple cider vinegar (1 tbsp.)
- Granulated sweetener (1 tbsp.)

- Veggie broth (2 cups)
- Rolls, slices of bread or lettuce wraps - for serving

Preparation Method:

1. Mix all of the fixings together in a pot or Dutch oven using the med-low heat. Cover and cook for about 45 minutes, occasionally stirring, until the vegetable broth is completely absorbed.

2. Check on the sloppy joe mixture along the way, to make sure that it is simmering, but not burning.

3. Serve on keto rolls or bread.

Chapter 10: Delicious Side Dishes & Appetizers

Side Dishes

Broccoli & Mushrooms - Instant Pot - Vegan

Yields Provided: 4

Nutritional Facts Per Serving:

- **Protein Count**: 2.1 grams
- **Total Fat Content**: 7 grams
- **Net Carbohydrates**: 2.3 grams
- **Calorie Count**: 80.7

Ingredients Needed:

- Sliced mushrooms (1 cup)
- Broccoli florets (2 cups)
- Coconut oil (1 tbsp.)
- Veggie broth (1 cup)
- Soy sauce (1 tbsp.)

Preparation Method:

1. Choose the saute function and add the coconut oil to the Instant Pot to melt.

2. When it's hot, toss in the mushrooms to saute for about 4-5 minutes.
3. Stir in the soy sauce and broccoli. Continue cooking for one more minute.
4. Empty in the broth and secure the lid of the cooker.
5. Use the high setting and set the timer for two minutes.
6. Quick-release the pressure when done.
7. Serve the veggies with a spritz of the cooking juices.

Carrot & Sweet Potato Medley - Instant Pot - Vegan

Yields Provided: 4

Nutritional Facts Per Serving:

- **Protein Count**: 7 grams
- **Total Fat Content**: 7.5 grams
- **Net Carbohydrates**: 6.3 grams
- **Calorie Count**: 413

Ingredients Needed:

- Cubed sweet potatoes (2 lb.)
- Olive oil (2 tbsp.)

- Onion (1)
- Baby carrots - halved (2 lb.)
- Vegetable broth (1 cup)

Preparation Method:

1. Warm up the Instant Pot using the saute function.
2. Pour in the olive oil into the cooker. Chop the onion and toss into the pot. Sauté until softened, about 5 minutes.
3. Cut the carrots in half and stir in the rest of the fixings.
4. Close the top.
5. Use the manual setting on high for 8 minutes.
6. Quick-release the pressure and serve.

Creamy Green Cabbage

Yields Provided: 4

Nutritional Facts Per Serving:

- **Protein Count**: 4 grams
- **Total Fat Content**: 42 grams
- **Net Carbohydrates**: 8 grams
- **Calorie Count**: 432

Ingredients Needed:

- Vegan butter (2 oz.)
- Shredded green cabbage (1.5 lb.)
- Coconut cream (1.25 cups)
- Finely chopped fresh parsley (8 tbsp.)
- Pepper and salt (as desired)

Preparation Method:

1. Prepare a skillet using the butter. Shred the cabbage and add to a skillet. Sauté until golden brown.
2. Stir in the cream, salt, and pepper. Simmer.
3. Garnish using the parsley and serve warm.

Instant Pot Ratatouille - Vegan

Yields Provided: 4

Nutritional Facts Per Serving:

- **Protein Count**: 2.5 grams
- **Total Fat Content**: 10 grams
- **Net Carbohydrates**: 7.1 grams
- **Calorie Count**: 180

Ingredients Needed:

- Eggplants (2 small or 1 medium)
- Medium zucchini (2)
- Sliced tomatoes (3)

- Olive oil (1 tbsp.)
- Water – for the pot (1-2 cups)

Preparation Method:

1. Pour the water into the Instant Pot.
2. Slice the zucchini and eggplant. Prepare a baking dish with a layer of zucchini, tomatoes, and eggplant on the top.
3. Continue to layer until finished. Spritz with oil and arrange the dish on the trivet in the cooker.
4. Secure the lid and set the timer for 10 minutes using the high setting.
5. Natural-release for about 10 minutes. Open and serve.

Mexican Cauli-Rice

Yields Provided: 4

Nutritional Facts Per Serving:

- **Protein Count**: 4 grams
- **Total Fat Content**: 8 grams
- **Net Carbohydrates**: 5 grams
- **Calorie Count**: 121

Ingredients Needed:

- White onion (half of 1 medium)
- Garlic (1 clove)

- Olive oil (2 tbsp.)
- Cumin (1 tsp.)
- Chili powder (1 tbsp.)
- Riced cauliflower (1 lb.)
- Diced tomatoes – no salt (14.5 oz. can)
- Pink Himalayan salt (as desired)

Preparation Method:

1. Use the medium temperature heat setting on the stovetop to warm the oil.
2. Dice the garlic and onion, and toss them into the pan. Sauté for 2-3 minutes. When they're soft, add the spices and continue sautéing for about 30 seconds.
3. Toss in the riced cauliflower. Sauté for another five to seven minutes until it's starting to get crispy around the edges (similar to fluffed rice).
4. Add salt and serve. Garnish using jalapenos, sour cream, cilantro, avocado, or a splash of lime.
5. You can keep it in the fridge for about four days.

Okra Indian Stir Fry - Vegan

Yields Provided: 6

Nutritional Facts Per Serving:

- **Protein Count**: 2.9 grams
- **Total Fat Content**: 15.4 grams
- **Net Carbohydrates**: 5.4 grams
- **Calorie Count**: 164.7

Ingredients Needed:

- Okra (1 lb.)
- Olive oil/mustard (.25 cup)
- Large onion (1)
- Cumin seeds (1 tsp.)
- Turmeric (.5 tsp.)
- Dried red chilies (2)
- Salt (to your liking)

Preparation Method:

1. Warm the mustard/oil in a skillet until it starts smoking.
2. Cool it slightly and toss in the onions to sauté until they are a reddish-brown.
3. Rinse the okra, pat dry with paper towels, and cut into small pieces.

4. Sprinkle the onions with the chilies and cumin. Fold in the turmeric and okra.

5. Toss into the skillet and soften.

6. Once it's done, dust with salt, and serve. Serve with some Indian naan or a dish or rice.

Roasted Veggies

Yields Provided: 6

Nutritional Facts Per Serving:

- **Protein Count**: 2 grams
- **Total Fat Content**: 5 grams
- **Net Carbohydrates**: 3 grams
- **Calorie Count**: 65

Ingredients Needed:

- Large grape tomatoes (8)
- Chopped asparagus spears (10)
- Button mushrooms (1 cup)
- Sliced zucchini (2)
- Chopped yellow pepper (1)
- Olive oil (2 tbsp.)
- Lemon juice (1 tbsp.)
- Salt (.5 tsp.)

Preparation Method:

1. Set the oven temperature at 450º Fahrenheit. Lightly grease a baking pan.
2. Slice or chop the vegetables and toss them into the prepared pan.
3. Squeeze the lemon for the juice. Toss the veggies with the prepared mixture of oil and fresh juice.
4. Sprinkle with the salt and roast 40 minutes.
5. Serve when it's perfect for your taste.

Spinach & Cauliflower Bowl

Yields Provided: 1

Nutritional Facts Per Serving:

- **Protein Count**: 17 grams
- **Total Fat Content**: 40 grams
- **Net Carbohydrates**: 7 grams
- **Calorie Count**: 499

Ingredients Needed:

- Garlic (.25 tbsp.)
- Cauliflower (.75 cups)
- Almonds (.25 cup)
- Cilantro (.5 cup)

- Sunflower seeds (.5 tbsp.)
- Olive oil (2 tbsp.)

Preparation Method:

1. Chop the garlic and cauliflower.
2. Warm up the oven to 375° Fahrenheit.
3. Add the almonds on a baking tray to roast for 7 to 10 minutes. Set aside to cool.
4. Toss the cauliflower into a food processor and pulse until it's rice-like.
5. In a skillet, warm one tablespoon of oil using the medium temperature setting. Toss in the riced cauliflower and garlic. Sauté until golden brown dusting with pepper and salt.
6. Toss in the cilantro and spinach, but don't stir. Let the spinach wilt on top for two to three minutes.
7. Garnish with the sunflower seeds, and almonds before serving.

Bread Options

Brown Bread

Yields Provided: 16

Nutritional Facts Per Serving:

- **Protein Count**: 11.9 grams
- **Total Fat Content**: 8.8 grams
- **Net Carbohydrates**: 1.9 grams
- **Calorie Count**: 137

Ingredients Needed:

- Instant yeast (1 tsp.)
- Salt (1 pinch)
- Sugar or inulin (2 tbsp.)
- Baking powder (1 tsp.)
- Almond flour (2.5 cups)
- Whey protein isolate (2 cups)
- Xanthan gum (1 tbsp.)
- Warm water (1.25 cups)
- *Also Needed*: 9 by 5-inch loaf pan

Preparation Method:

1. Warm the oven to reach 375° Fahrenheit. Lightly spritz the loaf pan with cooking oil or use a sheet of parchment paper.
2. Whisk the dry fixings, including the instant yeast.
3. Slowly pour in warm water and whisk until it's a thick batter. Scoop the batter into the pan.

4. Put a kitchen tea towel over the pan and place it in a warm place to rise until the dough doubles in size (45 min.).
5. Sprinkle water over the dough tops. Bake the bread for 20-25 minutes. Serve piping hot.

Chapter 11: Snack Time Options

Coconut Granola Bars

Yields Provided: 8

Nutritional Facts Per Serving:

- **Protein Count**: 14.2 grams
- **Total Fat Content**: 12.7grams
- **Net Carbohydrates**: 0.7 grams
- **Calorie Count**: 102

Ingredients Needed:

- Flaxseed eggs (2)
- Medjool dates (4 chopped)
- Sea salt (.5 tsp.)
- Baking powder (.5 tsp.)
- Chia seeds (2 tbsp.)
- Vanilla beans (2 tsp. ground)
- Coconut (.25 cup - shredded)
- Flax meal (.25 cup)
- Coconut butter (.5 cup)
- Pure maple syrup (.5 cup)
- Rolled oats (1.5 cups - gluten-free)

Preparation Method:

1. Prepare the flax eggs. For 2 eggs, mix 6 tablespoons of water with 2 tablespoons of flax seeds.

2. Add the oats, flax meal, shredded coconut, ground vanilla beans, and baking powder together in a small bowl and combine thoroughly.

3. Separately, combine the maple syrup, dates, and flax eggs in another bowl.

4. Mix the two bowls together and combine the fixings thoroughly.

5. Grease the slow cooker and line it with parchment paper.

6. Toss all of the fixings into the slow cooker and pat it down, taking care to make sure it is distributed evenly. Adjust the slow cooker temperature to low and leave it be, covered for about 2.5 hours. You will know it is done when the middle ceases to be mushy.

7. After the bars have finished cooking, remove them by gently pulling out the parchment paper.

8. Let the results cool 40 minutes before cutting them into bars.

Garlic - Almond & Onion Chili Crackers - Vegan

Yields Provided: 14 crackers

Nutritional Facts Per Serving:

- **Protein Count**: 1.9 grams
- **Total Fat Content**: 4.3 grams
- **Net Carbohydrates**: 0.8 grams
- **Calorie Count**: 50

Ingredients Needed:

- Almond flour (1 cup)
- Flax meal or ground flaxseed (1 tbsp.)
- Water (3 tbsp.)
- Sea salt (.25 tsp.)

Optional Spices (.25 tsp. of each)

- Garlic powder
- Paprika
- Onion powder or flakes
- Cumin
- Chili powder (.125 tsp.)

Preparation Method:

1. Warm the oven ahead of time to reach 370° Fahrenheit.
2. Whisk each of the fixings together for the dough (1 min.). Mix in the fiber from the flax meal to absorb the water.
3. Shape into a ball and set aside for about ten minutes.
4. Arrange the dough on a layer of parchment baking paper, shaping it into a rectangle. Place another sheet on top. Flatten thinly and slice into crackers using a butter knife.
5. (Dip the knife blade into the water to help the edge from sticking).
6. Leave the bottom layer of paper under the dough and bake for 20-30 minutes. After that time, check at 5-minute intervals.
7. Cool on a wire rack for crispy crackers. Store for no more than ten days in the pantry.
8. Storage in the fridge will cause them to soften.

Chapter 12: Beverages & Smoothies

Pumpkin Spice Latte

Yields Provided: 1

Nutritional Facts Per Serving:

- **Protein Count**: 0.5 grams
- **Total Fat Content**: 23 grams
- **Net Carbohydrates**: 1 gram
- **Calorie Count**: 216

Ingredients Needed:

- Boiling water (1 cup)
- Instant coffee powder (1-2 tsp.)
- Pumpkin pie spice or cinnamon (1 tsp.)
- Unsalted butter (1 oz.)
- Also Suggested: Immersion Blender

Preparation Method:

1. Mix the instant coffee, spices, and butter in a mixing container.
2. Add water and blend for 20-30 seconds until foamy.
3. Pour into the cup and sprinkle using the spice.

4. Serve with a dollop of whipped cream as desired.

Vegan Whipped Cream

Yields Provided: 4

Nutritional Facts Per Serving:

- **Protein Count**: 2 grams
- **Total Fat Content**: 22 grams
- **Net Carbohydrates**: 9.5 grams
- **Calorie Count**: 246

Ingredients Needed:

- Coconut cream (14 oz.)
- *Optional*: Powdered sugar (3 tbsp.)
- *Optional*: Vanilla extract (1 tsp.)

Preparation Method:

1. Store the can of coconut cream into the coldest part of the fridge overnight.
2. When ready to use, carefully open it, but don't shake it. The cream part will separate from the water.
3. Scoop that out into the bowl of an electric mixer, leaving the water behind. You can use the water in a smoothie or trash it.

4. Use the slow speed setting, and gradually increase the speed until you achieve a whipped cream consistency.

5. The harder the consistency of the cream when you scoop it out, the quicker the process.

6. Once you have whipped cream, you can stop since it's done. OR: Add a bit of powdered sugar and vanilla for a sweetened cream.

7. Whisk again until mixed in before serving.

Milk Shakes

Chocolate Chip Mint Shakes

Yields Provided: 2

Nutritional Facts Per Serving:

- **Protein Count**: 4 grams
- **Total Fat Content**: 21 grams
- **Net Carbohydrates**: 11 grams
- **Calorie Count**: 274

Ingredients Needed:

- Full-fat coconut milk (1 cup)
- Unsweetened dark chocolate – diced (2 tbsp.)
- Mint leaves (.5 cup)
- Pitted avocado (half of 1)

- Pure vanilla extract (1 tsp.)
- Sugar substitute or maple syrup (1 tbsp.)
- Ice (.5 cup)

Preparation Method:

1. Toss everything into a high-speed blender (like NutriBullet). Pulse until creamy smooth.
2. Serve immediately.
3. Add more ice if you like a thicker shake.

Turmeric Grain & Gluten-Free Milkshake

Yields Provided: 1

Nutritional Facts Per Serving:

- **Protein Count**: 1.6 grams
- **Total Fat Content**: 35.2 grams
- **Net Carbohydrates**: 5.5 grams
- **Calorie Count**: 351

Ingredients Needed:

- Non-dairy milk - ex. coconut milk (1.5 cups)
- Coconut oil (2 tbsp.)
- Ginger powder (.5 tsp.) or ½-inch peeled ginger root (.5-inch knob)
- Turmeric powder (.75 tsp.) or peeled turmeric root (3-inch piece)

- Cinnamon (.25 tsp.)
- Granulated sweetener of choice (as desired)
- Himalayan salt (1 pinch)
- Vanilla (.25 tsp.)
- Ice cubes (2)

Preparation Method:

1. Toss all of the fixings into a high-powered blender. If it's not high powered, mince the turmeric and ginger roots before adding them to the blender, or instead use powdered turmeric and ginger.
2. Blend using the high setting for 30 seconds or until thick and golden.
3. Pour the keto turmeric milkshake into a glass and garnish with cinnamon and turmeric.

Smoothies

Avocado Mint Green Smoothie

Yields Provided: 1

Nutritional Facts Per Serving:

- **Protein Count**:1 gram
- **Total Fat Content**: 23 grams
- **Net Carbohydrates**: 5 grams

- **Calorie Count**: 223

Ingredients Needed:

- Almond milk (.5 cup)
- Full-fat coconut milk (.75 cup)
- Avocado (3-4 oz. *or* half of 1)
- Cilantro (3 sprigs)
- Large mint leaves (5-6)
- Vanilla extract (.25 tsp.)
- Lime juice (1 squeeze)
- Sweetener of your choice (as desired)
- Crushed ice (1.5 cups)

Preparation Method:

1. Toss all of the fixings into the blender.
2. Combine using the low-speed setting until pureed.
3. Add in the ice and mix. Serve in a chilled glass.

Blueberry - Banana Bread Smoothie

Yields Provided: 2

Nutritional Facts Per Serving:

- **Protein Count**: 3.1 grams
- **Total Fat Content**: 23.3 grams
- **Net Carbohydrates**: 4.7 grams

- **Calorie Count**: 270

Ingredients Needed:

- Vanilla unsweetened coconut milk (2 cups)
- Blueberries (.25 cup)
- MCT oil (2 tbsp.)
- Liquid stevia (10 drops)
- Xanthan gum (.25 tsp.)
- Banana extract (1.5 tsp.)
- Chia seeds (1 tbsp.)
- Golden flaxseed meal (3 tbsp.)
- Ice cubes (2-3)

Preparation Method:

1. Add all of the fixings into a blender.
2. Wait a few minutes for the seeds and flax to absorb part of the liquid.
3. Pulse for one or two minutes until well combined.
4. Add the ice as desired.

Chocolate Mint Smoothie

Yields Provided: 1

Nutritional Facts Per Serving:

- **Protein Count**: 5 grams
- **Total Fat Content**: 40 grams

- **Net Carbohydrates**: 6.5 grams
- **Calorie Count**: 401

Ingredients Needed:

- Coconut milk (.25 cup)
- Unsweetened cashew/almond milk (1 cup)
- Swerve/erythritol (2 tbsp.)
- Cocoa powder (1 tbsp.)
- Fresh mint leaves (3-4)
- MCT oil (1 tbsp.)
- Ice cubes (2-3)
- Medium avocado (half of 1)
- Optional: Coconut milk or whipped cream

Preparation Method:

1. Mix all of the fixings in your blender.
2. Toss in the ice cubes. Add the toppings as desired.
3. Serve and enjoy!

Cinnamon Chia Smoothie

Yields Provided: 1

Nutritional Facts Per Serving:

- **Protein Count**: 23.6 grams
- **Total Fat Content**: 40.3 grams

- **Net Carbohydrates**: 4.7 grams
- **Calorie Count**: 467

Ingredients Needed:

- Cinnamon (.5 tsp.)
- Coconut milk (.5 cup)
- Ground chia seeds (1 tbsp.)
- Plain or vanilla whey protein (.25 cup)
- Water (.5 cup)
- Extra-virgin coconut oil or MCT oil (1 tbsp.)
- Optional: Stevia drops (to taste)

Preparation Method:

1 Pour the milk, cinnamon, protein powder, and chia seeds in a blender.
2 Add coconut oil, water, and ice. Add a few drops of stevia.
3   Pulse and serve.

Cinnamon Roll Smoothie

Yields Provided: 1

Nutritional Facts Per Serving:

- **Protein Count**: 26.5 grams
- **Total Fat Content**: 3.25 grams
- **Net Carbohydrates**: 0.6 grams

- **Calorie Count**: 145

Ingredients Needed:

- Vanilla protein powder (2 tbsp.)
- Flax meal (1 tsp.)
- Almond milk (1 cup)
- Vanilla extract (.25 tsp.)
- Sweetener (4 tsp.)
- Cinnamon (.5 tsp.)
- Ice (1 cup)

Preparation Method:

1. Combine each of the fixings in a blender.
2. Add the ice last.
3. Blend using the high setting for 30 seconds or until thickened.

Cucumber & Spinach Smoothie

Yields Provided: 2

Nutritional Facts Per Serving:

- **Protein Count**: 10.1 grams
- **Total Fat Content**: 32.4 grams
- **Net Carbohydrates**: 3 grams
- **Calorie Count**: 330

Ingredients Needed:

- Coconut milk (1 cup)
- MCT oil (2 tbsp.)
- Cucumber (2.5 oz.)
- Spinach (2 handfuls)
- Xanthan gum (.25 tsp.)
- Ice cubes (6)
- Your choice of sweetener (as desired)

Preparation Method:

1. Cream the coconut milk. This is a simple process. Store the can of coconut milk in the refrigerator overnight.
2. The next morning, open the can and scoop out the coconut milk that has solidified. Don't shake the can before opening. Discard the liquids.
3. Add all of the ingredients (omitting the ice cubes for now) into the blender.
4. Blend using low speed until pureed. Thin with water as needed.
5. Toss in the ice cubes into the blender and mix until the smoothie reaches your desired consistency.

Delicious Avocado Raspberry Smoothie

Yields Provided: 2

Nutritional Facts Per Serving:

- **Protein Count**: 2.5 grams
- **Total Fat Content**: 20 grams
- **Net Carbohydrates**: 4 grams
- **Calorie Count**: 227

Ingredients Needed:

- Unsweetened - frozen raspberries/or choice of berries (.5 cup)
- Your choice sugar equivalent (1 tbsp. + 1 tsp.)
- Ripe avocado (1)
- Lemon juice (3 tbsp.)
- Water (1.33 cups)

Preparation Method:

1. Mix all of the ingredients in a blender until smooth.
2. Pour the smoothie into two chilled glasses and serve.

Chapter 13: Delicious Fat Bombs

Sweet Bombs

Almond Fat Bombs - Vegan

Yields Provided: 10

Nutritional Facts Per Serving:

- **Protein Count**: 1 gram
- **Total Fat Content**: 13 grams
- **Net Carbohydrates**: 1 gram
- **Calorie Count**: 127

Ingredients Needed:

- Superfine almond flour (.5 cup)
- Melted coconut oil (.5 cup)
- Vanilla extract (1 tsp.)
- Almond extract (.5 tsp.)
- Stevia (16 drops)
- Salt (1 pinch)
- *Optional:* Sliced almonds (20)

Preparation Method:

1. Combine all of the fixings using a tablespoon to fill mini cupcake liners in a cupcake pan, silicone molds, or an ice cube tray with 2 tablespoonfuls in each.
2. Freeze for 15 minutes, and remove before totally frozen.
3. Top each fat bomb with 2 sliced almonds. (Almonds should sink into the top of the fat bombs.)
4. Freeze for one more hour. Either leave them in the trays or pop them out using hot water. Toss into freezer bags.
5. Enjoy when you want a delicious treat.

Cardamom Cinnamon Fat Bombs

Yields Provided: 10

Nutritional Facts Per Serving:

- **Protein Count**: 0.4 grams
- **Total Fat Content**: 10 grams
- **Net Carbohydrates**: 0.4 grams
- **Calorie Count**: 90

Ingredients Needed:

- Vegan - unsalted - unchilled butter (3 oz.)

- Unsweetened shredded coconut (.5 cup)
- Ground cinnamon (.25 tsp.)
- Ground cardamom - green (.25 tsp.)
- Vanilla extract (.5 tsp.)

Preparation Method:

1. Be sure the butter is room temperature.
2. Roast the shredded coconut until lightly browned and let it cool.
3. Combine half of the coconut and butter together with the spices.
4. Shape into ten portions and roll in the rest of the coconut.
5. Place in the freezer until ready to eat.

Cashew & Cacao Fat Bombs - Vegan

Yields Provided: 20

Nutritional Facts Per Serving:

- **Protein Count**: 4 grams
- **Total Fat Content**: 11 grams
- **Net Carbohydrates**: 6 grams
- **Calorie Count**: 133

Ingredients Needed:

- Raw cashews (1 cup)

- Cacao powder (.5 cup)
- Almond butter (1 cup)
- Coconut flour (.25 cup)
- Coconut oil (1 cup)

Preparation Method:

1. Heat a saucepan using the medium temperature setting on the stovetop. Pour in the coconut oil and almond butter. Stir well until mixed evenly.
2. Pour the oil mixture from the pan into a bowl. Mix in the coconut flour and cacao powder.
3. Place the mixing bowl in the freezer until the mixture cools and is solid (15-20 min.).
4. Meanwhile, toss the cashews into a food processor and pulse lightly for a chopped texture.
5. When the coconut mixture is solidified, take .5 tbsp. of the mixture from the bowl. Roll it into a ball and dip in the blended cashews.
6. Arrange the fat bombs on a plate. Continue until done.
7. Chill in the freezer for at least five minutes before enjoying.

Chocolate Peanut Butter Fat Bombs

Yields Provided: 12

Nutritional Facts Per Serving:
- **Protein Count**: 1.7 grams
- **Total Fat Content**: 8.7 grams

- **Net Carbohydrates**: 1.1 grams
- **Calorie Count**: 88

Ingredients Needed:

- Coconut oil (.25 cup)
- Sugar-free peanut butter (.25 cup)
- Unsweetened baking chocolate (1 oz.)
- Cocoa (1 tbsp.)
- Stevia drops – vanilla (.5 tsp.)

Preparation Method:

1. Use a double boiler to melt the peanut butter, oil, cocoa, and baking chocolate.
2. Take the pan from the burner and add the stevia.
3. Pour the mix into the molds to freeze.
4. When hard, store a closed plastic bowl in the freezer.

Dark Chocolate Fat Bombs

Yields Provided: 12

Nutritional Facts Per Serving:

- **Protein Count**: 4 grams
- **Total Fat Content**: 10.5 grams
- **Net Carbohydrates**: 5.6 grams
- **Calorie Count**: 96

Ingredients Needed:

- Stevia extract (1 tsp.)
- Butter/coconut oil (.5 cup)
- Almond butter (.5 cup)
- Dark chocolate – 85% or higher (3 oz.)
- Sea salt (.25 tsp.)

Preparation Method:

1. Mix all of the fixings until smooth using a double boiler.
2. Empty the mixture into 12 ice trays. Freeze for at least one hour.
3. Serve whenever you desire.

Walnut Orange Chocolate Bombs - Vegan

Yields Provided: 8

Nutritional Facts Per Serving:

- **Protein Count**: 2 grams
- **Total Fat Content**: 9 grams
- **Net Carbohydrates**: 2 grams
- **Calorie Count**: 87

Ingredients Needed:

- Extra-virgin coconut oil (.25 cup)
- Orange peel or orange extract (.5 tbsp.)

- Walnuts (1.75 cups - chopped)
- Cinnamon (1 tsp.)
- Stevia (10-15 drops)
- 85% Cocoa dark chocolate (12.5 grams)

Preparation Method:

1. Melt chocolate with your choice of method.
2. Add cinnamon and coconut oil. Sweeten mixture with stevia.
3. Pour in fresh orange peel and chopped walnuts.
4. In a muffin tin or in candy cup, spoon in the mixture.
5. Place into the fridge for one to three hours until the mixture is solid.

Other Bombs

Olive & Tomato Fat Bomb

Yields Provided: 5

Nutritional Facts Per Serving:

- **Protein Count**: 3.7 grams
- **Total Fat Content**: 17.1 grams
- **Net Carbohydrates**: 1.7 grams
- **Calorie Count**: 164

Ingredients Needed:

- Salt (.25 tsp.)
- Black pepper (as desired)
- Garlic (2 cloves)
- Kalamata olives (4)
- Sun-dried tomatoes (4 pieces)
- Oregano (2 tbsp.)
- Thyme (2 tbsp.)
- Basil (2 tbsp.)
- Coconut oil (.25 cup)
- Coconut cream (.5 cup)
- Cheese substitute - See Recipe (8 oz.)

Preparation Method:

1. Prep the veggies. Mince the garlic and chop the spices (basil, thyme, and oregano). Drain the tomatoes and remove the pits from the olives.

2. Add the coconut oil to a small mixing bowl with the cream and leave them both to soften for about 30 minutes. Mash together and mix well to combine.

3. Add in Kalamata olives and sun-dried tomatoes and mix well before adding in the herbs and seasonings. Combine thoroughly before placing

the mixing bowl in the refrigerator to allow the results to solidify.

4. Once it has solidified, form the mixture into a total of 5 balls using an ice cream scoop. Roll each of the finished balls in cheese substitute before plating.

5. Extras can be stored in the refrigerator in an airtight container for up to 7 days.

Chapter 14: Tempting Desserts

Cake Options

Almond Butter Cupcakes

Yields Provided: 4

Nutritional Facts Per Serving:

- **Protein Count**: 6.1 grams
- **Total Fat Content**: 16 grams
- **Net Carbohydrates**: 3.5 grams
- **Calorie Count**: 183

Ingredients Needed:

- Unchilled - unsweetened almond butter (.25 cup)
- Unsweetened almond milk or your choice (.25 cup)
- Granulated sweetener (2 tbsp.)
- Ground flax seeds (2 tbsp.)
- Cocoa powder (2 rounded tbsp.)
- Baking powder (.5 tsp.)

The Frosting:

- Vegan keto cream cheese (2 tbsp.)

- Unsweetened almond milk (1-2 tbsp.)
- Unsweetened creamy almond butter (1 tbsp.)
- *Optional*: Extracts - stevia or coloring

Preparation Method:

1. Set the oven temperature at 350° Fahrenheit.
2. Line four wells of a standard-size muffin tin using paper liners.
3. Whisk the almond butter and almond milk until well combined. Stir in the sweetener and flaxseed. Set aside for now.
4. In another mixing bowl, use a fork to whisk the cocoa powder and baking powder together until thoroughly combined.
5. Fold the dry fixings into the wet, and continue to stir until no lumps remain.
6. Divide the batter evenly among the four muffin wells, filling each about three-quarters full. Bake for 30 minutes, or until firm to the touch.
7. Remove from the oven and cool in the pan for at least 20 minutes for the cupcakes to set. Remove from the pan and cool completely before frosting.

8. Prepare the frosting. Pour the cream in a small mixing bowl. Stir in the almond butter, almond milk, and any optional flavoring or coloring.

Pudding

Pumpkin & Almond Pudding

Yields Provided: 10

Nutritional Facts Per Serving:

- **Protein Count**: 6 grams
- **Total Fat Content**: 16 grams
- **Net Carbohydrates**: 4 grams
- **Calorie Count**: 154

Ingredients Needed:

- Coconut oil (5 oz.)
- Pumpkin puree (10 oz.)
- Coconut cream (5 oz.)
- Pumpkin pie spice (1 tbsp.)
- Powdered erythritol (3 tbsp.)
- Almonds (4 oz.)
- Ginger (.75 tsp.)

Preparation Method:

1. Combine and stir all of the fixings (omit the almonds for now) in a saucepan using the medium heat setting (10 minutes).
2. Pour the mixture into silicone molds and press an almond inside each one.
3. Freeze for a minimum of one hour. Remove from the molds and serve or freeze for later.
4. For a taste change, just squeeze a little lemon juice over the pudding before serving.

Strawberry Coconut Chia Pudding - Vegan

Yields Provided: 3

Nutritional Facts Per Serving:

- **Protein Count**: 3.8 grams
- **Total Fat Content**: 21.5 grams
- **Net Carbohydrates**: 6.1 grams
- **Calorie Count**: 264

Ingredients Needed:

- Chia seeds (3 tbsp.)
- Almond milk (1 cup.)
- Vanilla extract (1 tsp.)
- Full-fat coconut milk - refrigerated (1 can)

The Jam:

- Frozen strawberries (1 cup)
- Coconut sugar (1 tsp.)

The Toppings:

- Strawberry jam (1 tsp.)
- Berries - fresh or frozen

Optional:

- Almond butter (1 tsp.)
- Passion fruit
- Quinoa puffs

Preparation Method:

1. Combine the almond milk, chia seeds, and vanilla in a jar or container. Stir and refrigerate overnight.
2. In the morning, remove from fridge.
3. Prepare the strawberry jam in a pan. Add frozen strawberries and coconut sugar. Cook on low for about 15 minutes. Let the strawberries melt and cook down.
4. Using an immersion blender, mix the jam until smooth and continue cooking for a couple of minutes to thicken. It will be tasty in the refrigerator for seven days.

5. Open a can of coconut milk and remove the solid cream. Save the leftover coconut water for smoothies. If the pudding is too thick, stir in a spoonful of coconut water or coconut milk.
6. Whisk the thick coconut cream.
7. Layer the pudding into jars. Begin with a layer of strawberry jam, a layer of chia pudding, and top it off with a layer of coconut milk. Repeat until you use up the fixings.
8. Top with a portion of strawberry jam and berries.
9. Optionally, you can add a teaspoon of almond butter, quinoa puffs, or passion fruit.
10. Serve for breakfast, dessert, or snack.

Delicious Pie

Chocolate Almond Butter Pie

Yields Provided: 12 slices

Nutritional Facts Per Serving:

- **Protein Count**: 6.5 grams
- **Total Fat Content**: 42.5 grams
- **Net Carbohydrates**: 5.1 grams

- **Calorie Count**: 359

Ingredients Needed:

The Crust:

- Coconut flour (.75 cup)
- Psyllium husk (2 tbsp.)
- Coconut oil (.5 cup)
- Water (.5 cup)
- Salt (1 pinch)

The Filling:

- 100% Unsweetened chocolate - Ghirardelli (2 oz.)
- Full-fat coconut milk (400 ml can)
- Coconut oil (.25 cup)
- Almond butter (1 cup)
- *Optional:* Stevia (.25 tsp.)

Preparation Method:

1. Heat the oven to reach 350° Fahrenheit.
2. Melt the coconut oil, water, and psyllium husk until a type of gel forms.
3. Stir in the flour and salt. Wait for 1-2 minutes or until all the liquid has been absorbed.

4. Press the crust into a 9-inch pie plate. Poke the bottom of the crust a few times with a fork to help release air, so the crust doesn't puff.

5. Bake for 30 minutes.

6. Meanwhile, mix the rest of the fixings in a high-speed blender. Process until they're thoroughly combined. (You can melt the chocolate first.)

7. Transfer the crust from the oven and cool it for a few minutes before pouring in the filling.

8. Chill in the fridge for 6 to 8 hours until set or freeze for 3 hours.

CONCLUSION

Keto is just one phase of a dieting plan. As a vegan, you will be taking it one step further.

If you are trying to change your lifestyle, it calls for immense commitment and hard work. It is quite easy to fall for loopholes and give up early or even halfway through because you cannot find the energy and motivation to handle the changes.

Set yourself easily achievable goals initially. Setting unachievable targets can put you off as you see yourself as a failure. Take a little at a time and be motivated by your small achievements. Slowly, you will see setting higher targets and achieve them too.

The Problem Of Consuming Protein Food Without Carbs

Studies are still being conducted concerning the risk of using a high-protein diet with carbohydrate restrictions for the long term. As time passes, a high-protein diet plan can create health issues. These are a few possibilities:

- For a diet consisting of full-fat dairy products used in many high-protein, your risk of heart disease can be increased.
- If you have kidney disease, you already have issues eliminating the waste products of protein metabolism. A high-protein diet may worsen the problems.
- High-protein diets and limited carbohydrates can result in nutritional deficiencies or insufficient fiber, which can cause issues including headache, bad breath, and constipation.

It's vital to consider the quality of the carbohydrates you eat. Remove all processed carbs from your diet, and choose the ones that are nutrient-dense and high in fiber, such as fruits, veggies, and whole grains.

Be sure to speak with your physician before you begin any weight-loss diet plan. Lastly, keep in mind; you must continue to eat wisely, or the weight loss may only be temporary. Dissuade the temptations and do not return to your previous eating habits.

Index For The Recipes

- Mushroom Omelet

Bagels

- Asiago Bagels
- Cheese Bagels
- Keto Vegan Bagels - Gluten-Free & Nut-Free
- Pizza Bagels
- Sesame - Poppy Seed Bagels

Tasty Biscuits

- Bacon Cheddar Drop Biscuits

- ## Lavender Biscuits

- "Red Lobster" Faux Low-Carb Biscuits
- 3-Minute Biscuits
- Zucchini Gluten-Free Cheesy Drop Biscuits

Pancakes - French Toast - Waffles & More

- Belgian Style Waffles

- ## Blueberry Ricotta Pancakes

- Lemon Waffles - Vegan
- Oven-Baked Bacon & Onion Pancake
- Tomato Pesto Mug Cake - Brunch

Cereal Options

- Blueberry Overnight Oatmeal
- Coconut Oatmeal
- Muesli Cereal

Chapter 8: Salad & Soup Specialties

Salad

- Asian Zucchini Salad
- Cauliflower Tabbouleh - Instant Pot
- Crunchy Cauliflower & Pine Nut Salad
- Ginger Walnut & Hemp Seed Lettuce Wraps
- Instant Pot Cauliflower & Rice Salad
- Salad Sandwiches
- Spicy Asian Cucumber Salad
- Steak Salad

Soups

- Asiago Tomato Soup
- Avocado Mint Chilled Soup
- Beef Curry - Slow-Cooker
- Cabbage Roll 'Unstuffed' Soup - Instant Pot
- Chicken "Zoodle" Soup
- Greens Soup
- Mexican-Cuisine Chicken Soup - Slow Cooker
- Pomodoro Soup - Instant Pot - Vegan

Chapter 9: Dinner Options

- Brussels Sprouts Spaghetti - Vegan

- Cauliflower Patties - Instant Pot - Vegan

- Cheeseburger Calzone

- Chicken Mozzarella & Pesto Casserole

- Chicken On A Skewer

- Creamy Salmon Pasta

- Garlic Spaghetti Squash - Vegan

- Keto Lo Mein - Vegan

- Lamb Chops & Herb Butter

- Keto Herb Butter

- Mini-Vegan Shepherd's Pie - Instant Pot

- Mixed Vegetable Vegan Patties -Instant Pot

- Peanut Ginger Cold Noodle Vegan Salad

- Ramen Vegan Noodles

- Steak Tacos - Slow-Cooked

- Stuffed Pork Chops

- Vegan-Inspired Sloppy Joes

Chapter 10 : Delicious Side Dishes & Bread Choices
Side Dishes

- Broccoli & Mushrooms - Instant Pot - Vegan

- Carrot & Sweet Potato Medley - Instant Pot - Vegan
- Cauliflower Mac & Cheese
- Creamy Green Cabbage
- Grain-Free Philly Cheesesteak Stuffed Peppers
- Instant Pot Ratatouille - Vegan
- Mexican Cauli-Rice
- Okra Indian Stir Fry - Vegan
- **Parmesan Onion Rings**
- Roasted Veggies
- Spinach & Cauliflower Bowl

Bread Options

- Brown Bread
- Cauliflower Bread
- **Coconut Flaxseed Bread**
- **Cornbread Muffins**
- **Garlic Bread**

Chapter 11 : Snack Time Options

- Air Fried - Bacon-Wrapped Chicken
- **Avocado - Tuna Melt Bites**
- Bacon Pickle Fries
- Bacon-Wrapped Mozzarella Sticks
- Broiled Bacon Wraps With Dates
- Caprese Snacks
- Caramelized Bacon Knots
- Cheese Roll-Ups
- Chocolate Dipped Candied Bacon
- Coconut Granola Bars
- Garlic - Almond & Onion Chili Crackers - Vegan
- Roasted Cauliflower With Blue Cheese Sauce
- Salmon & Cream Cheese Bites

Chapter 12: Beverages & Smoothies
- Bulletproof Coffee
- Coffee & Cream - Vegetarian
- Pumpkin Spice Latte
- Vegan Whipped Cream

Milk Shakes
- Chocolate Chip Mint Shakes
- Delicious Chocolate Shakes

- Peanut Butter Caramel Milkshake
- Turmeric Grain & Gluten-Free Milkshake

Smoothies

- Avocado Mint Green Smoothie
- Blueberry Almond Smoothie
- Blueberry - Banana Bread Smoothie
- Blueberry Yogurt Smoothie
- Chocolate Mint Smoothie
- Cinnamon Chia Smoothie
- Cinnamon Roll Smoothie
- Cucumber & Spinach Smoothie
- Delicious Avocado Raspberry Smoothie
- Strawberry Almond Smoothie

Chapter 13: Delicious Fat Bombs

Sweet Bombs

- Almond Fat Bombs - Vegan
- Cardamom Cinnamon Fat Bombs
- Cashew & Cacao Fat Bombs - Vegan
- Chocolate Chip Cookie Dough Fat Bomb
- Chocolate Peanut Butter Fat Bombs

- Dark Chocolate Fat Bombs

- No-Bake Lemon Cheesecake Fat Bombs
- Walnut Orange Chocolate Bombs - Vegan
- White Chocolate Fat Bomb - Vegetarian

Other Bombs
- Bacon Guacamole Fat Bombs
- Olive & Tomato Fat Bomb - Vegan
- Pizza Fat Bombs

Chapter 14: Tempting Desserts
Cake Options
- Almond Butter Cupcakes
- Blueberry Cupcakes
- Orange Rum Cake - Instant Pot
- Pumpkin Caramel Bundt Cake
- Zucchini Chocolate Cake

Pudding
- Cheesecake Pudding
- Crunch Berry Mousse
- Pumpkin & Almond Pudding
- Pumpkin Custard - Crockpot
- Strawberry Coconut Chia Pudding

Delicious Pie

- Banoffee Pie - Egg-Free
- Blueberry Cream Pie
- Chocolate Almond Butter Pie
- Creamy Lime Pie
- Lemon Sour Cream Pie
- Low-Carb Almond Flour Crust
- Pumpkin Cheesecake Pie
- Pumpkin Cream Pie
- Strawberry Cream Pie - No-Bake

Tasty Tarts

- Pistachio Dark Chocolate Tart
- Pumpkin Pecan Tarts

Made in the USA
Monee, IL
25 February 2023

28674579R00098